Light and Living Matter,
Volume 1: The Physical Part

Light and Living Matter: A Guide to the Study of Photobiology

Volume 1: The Physical Part

Roderick K. Clayton, Ph.D.

Professor of Biology and Biophysics
Cornell University

McGraw-Hill Book Company

New York, St. Louis, San Francisco, Düsseldorf,
London, Mexico, Panama, Sydney, Toronto

to my principal teachers:

Max Delbrück
C. B. van Niel
William Arnold

Light and Living Matter,
Volume 1: The Physical Part

Library of Congress Catalog Card Number: 75-114444

1 2 3 4 5 6 7 8 9 0 B A B A 7 9 8 7 6 5 4 3 2 1 0

This book was set in Times New Roman by Spottiswoode,
Ballantyne and Co. Ltd., and printed on permanent paper and
bound by George Banta Company, Inc. The designer was
Marsha Cohen; the drawings were done by Philip Cohen. The
editors were Jeremy Robinson and James W. Bradley. Matt
Martino supervised the production.

The Chemistry-Biology Interface Series

Several years ago, a few dozen biologists, chemists, physicists, and other scientists spent several days on the campus of the University of Washington under the joint sponsorship of the Commission on Undergraduate Education in Biological Sciences, the Advisory Council on College Chemistry, and the Commission on College Physics. The purpose was to study ways to improve teaching in areas of mutual concern to two or more of the disciplines involved. The group considering the area between chemistry and biology agreed that a series of paperback books, prepared for elementary college level students in either biology or chemistry could serve a useful purpose toward this end.

Prepared by authorities in their fields, these books could, for the chemists, indicate the biologically significant reactions useful to illustrate chemical principles and, for the biologist, summarize up-to-date information on molecular phenomena of significance to a modern understanding of biological systems.

To implement this proposal, CUEBS and AC_3 appointed an editorial committee of:

Professor Robert H. Burris, Department of Biochemistry, University of Wisconsin

Professor L. Carroll King, Department of Chemistry, Northwestern University

Professor Leonard K. Nash, Department of Chemistry, Harvard University

Professor Aubrey W. Naylor, Department of Botany, Duke Universtiy

Professor Charles C. Price, Department of Chemistry, University of Pennsylvania

to organize the undertaking.

As of this writing, the following volumes are in preparation:

O. T. Benfey, "Organic Reaction Mechanisms"
Myron Bender, "Catalysis"
Melvin Calvin, "Chemical Evolution"
Roderick K. Clayton, "Light and Living Matter: Volume II"
Paul M. Doty, "Macromolecules"
David E. Greene, "Surfaces, Films, and Membranes"
Charles C. Price, "Geometry of Molecules"

It is our hope that the material in these volumes will prove of sufficient interest to teachers and students in elementary college chemistry and biology courses that much of it will ultimately be incorporated in regular textbooks.

Charles C. Price
Philadelphia, Pennsylvania

Preface

This book will provide insight into the ways that light interacts with living things and into the techniques for studying such interactions. The purpose is to provide reading for undergraduate students at an interface between physics, chemistry, and biology, especially for use as an adjunct to courses in chemistry and biology. While this purpose has been kept primary, as the writing progressed it appeared that the book would be suitable also as a text for courses in photobiology or biological optics. Finally, because considerable practical material has been included, this book should be useful as an introductory guide to research in photochemistry and photobiology.

The general level of preparation for readers of this book should correspond to past or concurrent first-year courses in physics, chemistry, and mathematics (preferably calculus).

The book has been structured into two volumes: volume I, The Physical Part, and volume II, The Biological Part. After a short introductory chapter, volume I describes the nature of light as it interacts with matter (Chap. 2) and then imparts a working knowledge of methods in optics as used by chemists and biologists (Chap. 3 and the appendixes). Volume II treats the major systems and problems of photobiology from a contemporary investigative viewpoint. The topics include photosynthesis, phototaxis and phototropism, vision, the regulation of physiological activities by light, damaging effects of light, and bioluminescence.

The volumes are independent: volume I alone might be useful in a chemistry course and volume II in a biology course. The reading of volume II without volume I may, however, lead to a level of understanding that is more descriptive than analytical. Another possibility is to study both volumes more or less in parallel.

The problems at the end of Chap. 3 will allow the student to test his understanding of biological and chemical optics at a working level. There are disparities in the degree of difficulty of these problems, which reflects the usual state of affairs in the laboratory. The "easiest" and "most difficult" of these problems (an arbitrary classification by the author) are identified by * and †.

Certain limitations of content have proved to be desirable or unavoidable. The second chapter is merely a descriptive sketch, designed to make the subsequent material easier to visualize. It in no sense replaces a proper and thorough treatment of radiation physics. The language is often crude by the standards of quantum theory, and it is meant to convey sensible impressions without the satisfaction that comes with a rigorous treatment of the subject. No account is made of the theory and practice of polarization optics. The text is not annotated, but abundant references to the research literature can be found in the reviews and books that are recommended in the bibliographies at the ends of chapters.

Roderick K. Clayton

Contents

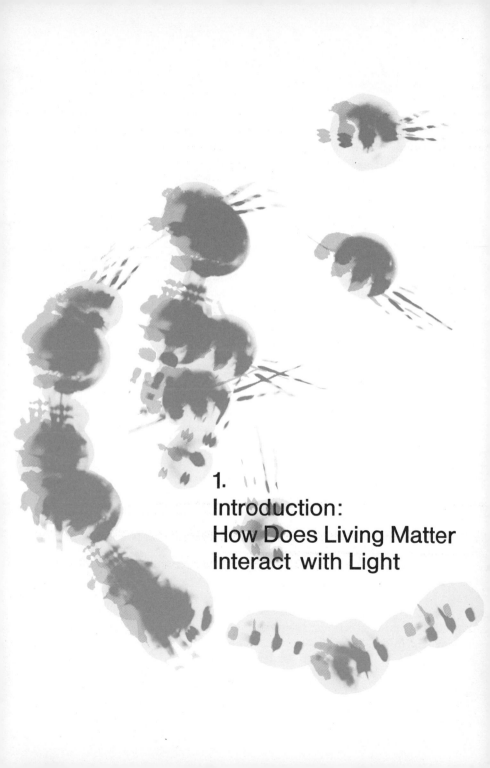

1.
Introduction:
How Does Living Matter
Interact with Light

Radiation from the sun has provided the energy to sustain all life on the earth. But light, from the point of view of living matter, is more than a source of energy. It is a means of sensing the environment, a signaling device, an indicator of the time of day and the season, and a poison.

As a source of energy sunlight has the obvious and direct role of maintaining the earth at a hospitable temperature. Radiation from the sun also supports the photosynthetic growth of plants and, indirectly, the lives of animals that eat plants, animals that eat animals that eat plants, animals that burn coal and oil, and so forth.

When utilized in a sensory mechanism (vision), light affords an exquisitely detailed, long-range, and practically instantaneous way for an organism to map its environment. Some primitive organisms such as bacteria and molds display a crude form of vision, responding to light stimuli with sudden movements (phototaxis) or growing toward or away from a source of light (phototropism).

Bioluminescence, the production of light by living things, is exhibited by a wide range of animals, bacteria, and fungi. Among fireflies different species emit differently timed sequences of light flashes. The signals emitted by members of one species attract the attention of the opposite sex of just that species. Here the luminescence has an obvious use, but in many cases (as with the luminous bacteria) the survival value of bioluminescence is not clear.

Many living things alter their appearance or their behavior at certain times of the year: birds migrate, insects change from larval to adult stages, and plants develop flowers. The most reliable signal that a season has arrived is the length of daylight (or of night), and this can be measured with a photochemical mechanism. Again, daily cycles of activity (feeding patterns, short-range migrations, sleep, intensity of luminescence, capacity to perform photosynthesis, and many others) are kept synchronous with the day-night cycle through photochemical mechanisms that record the arrival of dawn. There are also processes, such as the formation of skin pigment in animals and of chlorophyll in developing plants, that are controlled by light but are not especially related to the season or to a daily rhythm.

Finally we (and other forms of life) are susceptible to damage of our cellular constituents by ultraviolet light and also by visible light if a suitable light-absorbing dye (a sensitizer) and oxygen are present. Curiously enough, there are light-dependent mechanisms for repairing some of the damage caused by ultraviolet (photo-reactivation). We thus live in a balance between damage and repair, both induced by light.

Let us now consider the nature of light and of its interaction with matter and return later to a more detailed examination of these photobiological phenomena.

2.
The Physics of
Radiation and Matter

In this chapter we will develop conceptions of the nature of light, of the quantum descriptions of light and matter, and of the interaction between light and matter. For the most part the development will be descriptive; only in a few cases will relationships be formulated mathematically.

THE NATURE OF LIGHT

2-1. *Light as an Electromagnetic Wave*

One of the fundamental properties of matter is the force exerted by one electrically charged body on another. There are two kinds of such force, the electrostatic force and the magnetic force. The former is an attraction between charges of opposite sign and repulsion between like charges; it acts whether the charges are moving or at rest. The latter is exerted only among moving charges and is more complicated to describe in terms of its direction.

The action of one charge on another is not expressed instantaneously; it is communicated with a finite speed (the speed of light). Thus if a charged particle were created suddenly, its action on another charge would occur only after a certain time had elapsed.

The force that one set of charges will exert on others in its neighborhood can be mapped as a *force field*. At every point in space two vectors are drawn: an electric vector which gives the electrostatic force and a magnetic vector from which the magnetic force can be computed.[1] In describing light we shall be concerned with the force field that surrounds a particular configuration of charges, an oscillating electric dipole. In simplest terms a dipole is a pair of charged particles, one positive and the other negative, separated by a very small distance (small compared with the distance from which

---

[1] In physics a vector is a description that involves direction as well as magnitude. For example, a north wind of 10 miles per hour can be represented on a map by a velocity vector: an arrow pointing southward and having a length of ten units. Similarly the electrostatic force vector shows the direction and magnitude of this force. In the more complicated magnetic case, the vector does not show a force directly but provides a basis for computing the magnetic force on a moving charge.

the dipole is viewed). Imagine that the two charges oscillate along the line connecting them, so that their separation is a sine function of the time. Such an oscillating dipole generates a moving wavelike force field, as indicated in Fig. 2-1.[1] Taking any straight line that

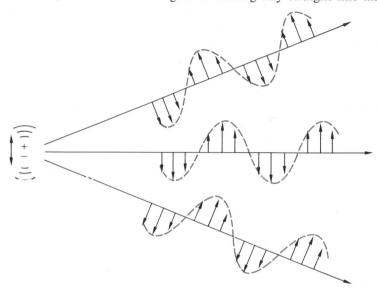

Fig. 2-1.   A representation of the electromagnetic wave radiated by an oscillating electric dipole. The electric vector is shown by the short arrows. The magnetic vector is not shown; it is perpendicular to and in phase with the electric vector. The pattern as a whole moves away from the dipole with the speed of light, its amplitude decreasing with distance.

radiates from the dipole, a map of the electric vector describes approximately a sine wave around this line. The wave lies in the same plane as the axis of the dipole, and the whole pattern moves away from the dipole with the speed of light. As the wave recedes, its amplitude diminishes in proportion to the distance from the dipole.

[1] The figure shows only the electric vector. The magnetic vector, which was omitted for the sake of simplicity, describes a wave that is everywhere perpendicular to and in phase with the wave of the electric vector.

This moving force field, generated by an oscillating dipole, is an example of an electromagnetic wave and is a description of light. It is also a description of radio waves, x-rays, and other types of radiation; what we call it depends on the frequency of oscillation of the dipole (and of the wave). If the frequency lies between 0.4×10^{15} and 0.75×10^{15} cycles/sec, the electromagnetic wave stimulates the

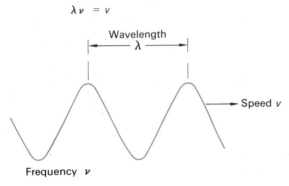

$$\lambda \nu = v$$

Fig. 2-2.   *The speed, frequency, and wavelength of a traveling wave are related by the expression* $\lambda \nu = v.$

pigment in our eyes and is perceived as visible light. Progressively higher frequencies are characterized as ultraviolet, x-rays, and gamma rays. At lower frequencies we encounter infrared (radiant heat), microwaves, and radio waves.

The speed of light in a vacuum is denoted c and equals 3×10^{10} cm/sec. In material media (such as air, glass, or water) the speed is reduced by a factor n: $v = c/n$. This factor, called the index of refraction, is characteristic of the material and depends also on the frequency of the wave. Its value lies between 1 and 2 for visible light in most transparent substances.

There is a simple relation, shown in Fig. 2-2, between the speed v, the frequency ν, and the wavelength λ of a wave: $\lambda \nu = v.$ This can be verified intuitively by considering the units of each quantity, for example,

$$\lambda \text{ (cm)} \times \nu \text{ (per sec)} = v \text{ (cm/sec)} \qquad (2\text{-}1)$$

This equation shows that if the speed changes, either the wavelength or the frequency must change. Actually the frequency of an electromagnetic wave is always that of the oscillating dipole, regardless of the medium, and the wavelength varies with the speed.

The wavelength of light is usually designated not in centimeters but in angstroms (1 Å = 10^{-8} cm) or in nanometers (1 nm = 10^{-9}m =

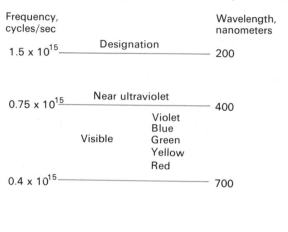

Fig. 2-3. Wavelengths and frequencies of light at the limits of the visible spectrum and adjacent regions. One nanometer (nm) equals 10^{-9} meter or 10 angstroms. Values of wavelength pertain to light in vacuum or in air where the speed is close to 3×10^{10} cm/sec.

10 Å). The nanometer is also called the millimicron (mμ). Wavelengths and frequencies in the vicinity of the visible spectrum are shown in Fig. 2-3 for light in vacuum or in air[1] where the speed is approximately equal to c.

An oscillating dipole is by no means the only configuration of moving charges that radiates an electromagnetic wave, but the dipole

---

[1] In colorless gases the index of refraction for visible light is close to unity so that v is approximately equal to c.

generates a wave that has an especially simple geometry. More complicated patterns (such as a negative charge moving in a circular orbit around a positive charge) can generally be built up by super-imposing two or more oscillating dipoles, and the radiation can then be described as a superposition of the waves radiated by the dipoles. This approach is useful when treating the motions of electrons in atoms and molecules and the consequent radiation of light.

Just as an oscillating dipole generates an electromagnetic wave, the wave (a pattern of electric forces) can in turn set other dipoles into oscillation of the same frequency. The process is roughly like the resonant vibration of one tuning fork in the presence of another, energy being communicated from one fork to the other through the medium of compression waves in the intervening matter. The electro-magnetic wave is thus a carrier of energy, as one can appreciate by standing in the sunshine. Work must be done in maintaining the oscillation of a dipole, a corresponding amount of energy is radiated into the surrounding space, and some of this energy is absorbed by other dipoles when they are set in motion. These other dipoles in turn radiate energy as a result of their oscillation. We can thus visualize the interaction of light with matter as a process in which energy is exchanged between a collection of oscillating dipoles and a radiation field. The oscillation of the dipoles corresponds to the movements of electrons relative to positively charged nuclei in matter.

When light passes through a transparent substance, one can imagine that the light is continually absorbed and reemitted with no net loss of energy. This process can be made to account for the reduced speed of light in a material medium.

2-2. Light as a Stream of Particles

The foregoing description of light, when given in a mathematically complete form, represented the highest development of electro-magnetic theory in the nineteenth century. Early in the present century it became clear that this theory could not treat properly the interaction between radiation and matter. Resolution of the difficulties, which we shall describe, led to a revision of our most basic ideas about the nature of observation and measurement and to the development of contemporary quantum theory.

One difficulty arose when the classical theory was applied to the problem of radiation by incandescent bodies. Such bodies were treated as collections of oscillating dipoles, of many strengths, orientations, and frequencies, in equilibrium with each other and with the radiation field surrounding them. The theory yielded a method for computing the rate at which an incandescent body radiates energy, and the computation yielded the nonsensical answer of infinity. In an effort to deal with this embarrassing problem, Planck suggested that a certain restriction be placed on the way that energy can be exchanged between the body and the radiation field: Energy can be exchanged only in discrete packets (quanta) proportional to the frequency of the radiation. The restriction can be written

$$E = h\nu \qquad\qquad (2\text{-}2)$$

where E is the energy of 1 quantum of frequency ν, and h is a universal natural constant (Planck's constant) equal to 6.6×10^{-27} erg sec. For light in vacuum one could also write, in view of Eq. (2-1),

$$E = \frac{hc}{\lambda} \qquad\qquad (2\text{-}3)$$

When subjected to this restriction, the theory gave a sensible answer that agreed with experiment.

Another trouble centered in the planetary model of an atom, in which a number of electrons move in orbits about a positively charged nucleus. Classical electromagnetic theory predicted that the electrons of an atom should radiate energy and should spiral into the nucleus as they lose energy. For any one type of atom the radiation should have a continuous range of frequencies rather than the highly distinctive set of frequencies that had already been observed in atomic spectra. Application of Planck's quantum hypothesis to this difficulty will be discussed later in this section.

Still another anomaly was unearthed by Einstein in his investigations of the photoelectric effect (see Fig. 2-4). Light impinging on a metal surface was observed to eject electrons from the metal. The electrons displayed a distribution of energies with a characteristic

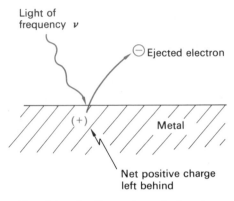

Fig. 2-4. An illustration of the photoelectric effect: Light shining on a metal surface ejects electrons having a variety of energies ranging from zero to E_{max}. The value of E_{max} is $h\nu - w$, where h is Planck's constant (6.6×10^{-27} erg sec), and w is a constant characteristic of the metal.

maximum value. Curiously enough the maximum value was found to be related not to the intensity of the light beam but to the frequency (or wavelength) of the light. Specifically Einstein found that

$$E_{max} = h\nu - w \qquad (2\text{-}4)$$

where h is Planck's constant, and w is a constant (the *work function*) characteristic of the metal. This result could be taken as direct experimental verification of Planck's quantum hypothesis. Packets of electromagnetic energy (light quanta) could be visualized crudely as bullets of energy $h\nu$ that shoot electrons out of the metal. The work function is interpreted as the energy needed to remove the electron against the attractive force of the net positive charge that is left behind in the metal. An ejected electron can thus have *at most* the energy of the quantum of light $h\nu$ that ejected it, diminished by the work function.

During the nineteenth century the atomic spectroscopists had compiled a large mass of data concerning the interactions of light with matter. It had been observed that atoms and simple molecules are highly selective with respect to the frequencies of light that they absorb and emit. A pure substance such as sodium vapor shows intense absorption at a number of well-defined frequencies and

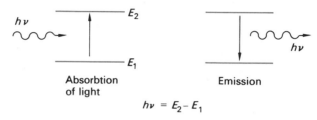

$$h\nu = E_2 - E_1$$

Fig. 2-5. Transitions of an atom between two states of characteristic energies E_1 and E_2 accompanied by absorption or emission of a quantum of light having the requisite energy.

negligible absorption elsewhere. The same substance can be heated to the point where it emits light; a spectrum of the emission shows many of the same "lines" or characteristic frequencies that appear in the absorption spectrum. This was taken to mean that in a given atom the dipole oscillations, performed by electrons and nuclei during absorption or emission of light, could have only certain frequencies.

Now the idea that radiation is quantized brought a new perspective to these facts. If a characteristic frequency ν is associated with a certain energy $h\nu$, the spectroscopic data can be evaluated in terms of definite energy states of the atoms. Absorption of light promotes an atom from a lower energy state to a higher one, one quantum supplying exactly the energy needed for the transition. A downward transition, from higher to lower energy, is similarly attended by the emission of a quantum having the appropriate energy. These processes are sketched in Fig. 2-5.

One of the chief early successes of the quantum theory was to predict, with a simple rule suggested by Bohr,[1] the allowable energy states of atoms and consequently the expected (and for the most part observed) wavelengths of the emission and absorption of light. Further development of the theory, in which the allowed states (*quantum states*) are described in more detail, has led to a description of the interactions between light quanta and atoms in terms of electric dipole oscillations that accompany transitions from one energy state to another. We shall return to these points later.

QUANTUM THEORY

2-3. *Some Consequences of the Quantum Hypothesis*

Having become convinced that radiant energy interacts with matter in the form of irreducible packets, or quanta, the physicists of the early twentieth century had to deal with some remarkable conceptual consequences of this idea. By earlier standards a system could be described to any desired degree of refinement if the positions and velocities of all its components were known with sufficient precision. The "mechanistic ideal" of the nineteenth century held that the past, present, and future of the universe could in principle be computed and described if all its elements were measured properly. But all physical measurements involve interactions between the observer and the system being observed. Information can reach the observer only

---

[1] Bohr's rule can be related to de Broglie's later suggestion that just as light has a particulate nature, the particles of matter have a wavelike character, with energy and frequency related according to $E = h\nu$. For an atomic electron, a particular orbit corresponds to a certain energy and·hence to a particular frequency and wavelength. Bohr postulated simply that for an orbit to be allowed, its circumference must equal a whole number of wavelengths of the electron. This rule restricts the number of possible orbits (and energies) to a discrete set. The wavelike nature of matter was first demonstrated by Davisson and Germer, who shot a narrow beam of electrons onto a screen where they could be detected. The distribution of electrons at the screen formed a diffraction pattern like that produced by the constructive and destructive interference of light waves in passing through a slit

through exchange of energy or matter, and if this medium of exchange is coarse grained (quantized), the information will be coarse grained also.

A suitable analysis,[1] starting with Planck's quantum hypothesis, shows that one cannot know simultaneously the exact position and the exact momentum (or velocity) of a system. Any measurement of position disturbs the momentum to an uncertain extent, and vice

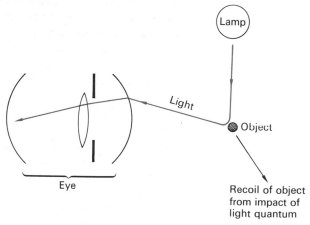

Fig. 2-6.   A sketch to illustrate a discussion of the uncertainty principle (see text).

versa. It follows that the future position of the system must also be uncertain, and that the mechanistic ideal of the nineteenth century cannot be retained.

These remarks can be illustrated as follows (see Fig. 2-6). To see an object, one must intercept quanta of light that have been reflected from or emitted by the object. For good optical resolution (accurate knowledge of position) the wavelength of the light must be small compared with the size of the object. A highly refined knowledge of position can thus be gained by using quanta of sufficiently small wavelength, but the less the wavelength, the greater is the energy of

[1] See the bibliography at the end of this chapter: texts on quantum theory.

each quantum, since $E = h\nu = hc/\lambda$ [see Eq. (2-3)]. Thus a smaller wavelength, chosen to improve the knowledge of position, leads to a greater recoil of the object when a quantum is reflected or emitted from it. An uncertainty is thus introduced into the observer's knowledge of the momentum of the object. Position and momentum are complementary in the sense that the more precisely one is determined, the less is known about the other. At this point one might argue that the recoil of the object could be computed from the path of the quantum reaching the eye. But the path of the quantum is also uncertain because the pupil of the eye is of finite size. If the pupil were made progressively smaller, so as to define the path of the quantum more perfectly, the diffraction of light at the pupil would have an ever greater effect in spoiling the image formed in the eye. As before, a better knowledge of momentum would go hand in hand with less knowledge of position, and vice versa. In this example, for objects large enough to be seen with the unaided eye, the uncertainty of position and momentum would be relatively small,[1] but the observational dilemma is revealed nevertheless.

Just as position and momentum are complementary, so are other pairs of physical parameters, notably energy and time. The better the energy of a system is defined, the less can be said about when the system has such an energy. In the extreme we can describe stationary states of atoms, molecules, and other systems. These are hypothetical states of definite energy and of indefinite duration. One can imagine that an atom is in one of these states, but any attempt at measurement can change the state in an unpredictable way.

2-4. Wave Functions

One task of quantum theory is to describe a set of permissible states for a system and then to assign probabilities that the system will be in one state or another under a given set of external circumstances. For any given allowable state of a system, parameters such as the positions and momenta of its components are again described by

---

[1] It can be shown that the uncertainty of position multiplied by the uncertainty of momentum is always greater than or equal to $h/2\pi$, where h is Planck's constant.

probability functions. The procedure, as applied to the allowed stationary states of a hydrogen atom, is somewhat as follows.[1] An equation (the Schrödinger wave equation) is written in a form appropriate to the problem at hand. Solutions of the equation yield a description of each of the permissible states of the atom, specifying

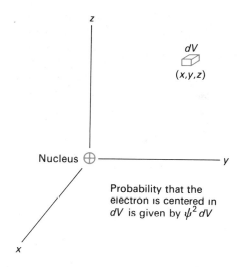

Probability that the electron is centered in dV is given by $\psi^2 dV$

Fig. 2-7. The nucleus of a hydrogen atom is placed at the center of a coordinate system (x, y, z). A wave function $\psi(x,y,z)$ maps the probability for position of the atom's single electron.

the total energy and giving a map of the positions of the electron relative to the nucleus. This map corresponds to the electron's orbit, but in quantum theory it has the form of a probability function.

The Schrödinger equation is a differential equation which in the present application contains the following elements: (1) space coordinates x, y, and z centered at the nucleus of the atom, as shown in Fig. 2-7 (in a description of stationary states, time does not appear

[1] For a treatment that goes beyond the primitive description given here, the reader should again consult an introductory text on quantum mechanics, as listed in the bibliography.

in the equation); (2) symbols that give instructions to perform differentiation with respect to the space coordinates; (3) constants including E, the total (internal) energy of the atom; and (4) a function ψ that will give a map of the position of the electron in terms of relative probability at each location (x,y,z). The function $\psi(x,y,z)$ is devised to be a *probability amplitude* for position of the electron. Its square gives the actual density of probability: If we consider a small[1] element of volume dV at (x,y,z) the probability of finding the electron in dV is given by $\psi^2\, dV$.

The probability amplitude ψ is commonly called a *wave function*. For an atomic electron in a stationary state of definite energy, this function has the form of a standing wave; and for a free electron (or, more generally, an electron in a time-varying state), ψ has the form of a traveling wave.

The form of the Schrödinger equation is such that solutions do not exist for all values of the energy, but only for a discrete set of values E_1, E_2, ... A quantized description of the atom, involving states having energies E_n ($n = 1$, 2, ...), is thus assured. Then for each of these quantized states the solution of the equation gives the appropriate wave function $\psi_n(x,y,z)$ which maps the position of the electron.

The foregoing description is superficial and incomplete, but for the present it is sufficient to show that the theory fulfills two requirements. First, it describes natural systems in terms of discrete sets of allowable states having different energies. Second, it recognizes the uncertainty principle by dealing in probabilities rather than certainties.

2-5. *Quantum States of Matter*

An atomic electron has well-defined quantum states as allowed and determined by the Schrödinger equation. A description of these states can be relatively crude or refined, according to the coarseness or delicacy with which the interactions of the electron with its surroundings are described.

---

[1] So small that ψ is effectively constant throughout the element dV.

If we consider only the electrostatic force between the electron and other charges in its neighborhood (especially the positively charged nucleus), we are led to a classification of major energy states E_n ($n = 1, 2, 3, \ldots$). These are the states predicted by Bohr's rule, mentioned in the last section. The *total quantum number n* is equivalent to a *shell* in the chemist's description: The innermost or K shell contains electrons for which $n = 1$, the L shell is for $n = 2$, and so forth. Increasing values of n correspond to progressively larger orbits in the classical picture.

The next refinement comes when magnetic forces between the electron and its surroundings are considered. For each quantum state the electron has a certain wave function that can be visualized loosely as an orbit or a style of movement. This movement, depending on its symmetry,[1] may or may not involve the electron in magnetic interactions with other moving charges. The capacity of the electron to interact magnetically by virtue of its orbital motion is called the *orbital magnetic moment*. It is specified by an indicial number l called the *azimuthal quantum number*: $l = 0, 1, 2, \ldots$, with increasing values denoting stronger magnetic moment (the moment is zero when l is zero). The outcome of the theory restricts l to whole-number values no greater than $n - 1$. Therefore the theory allows $l = 0$ for $n = 1$, $l = 0$ or 1 for $n = 2$, and so forth.

Each state characterized by a certain value of l is subdivided further into $2l + 1$ distinct states, based on the orientation of the electron's wave function relative to its surroundings. Thus for $l = 0$ there is just one such state because the wave function is spherically symmetric. For $l = 1$ there are $2l + 1$, or three, distinct orientations allowed by the theory, and so forth. This point is formalized by means of a *magnetic quantum number* m_l which is allowed any integral value from $-l$ through zero to $+l$. The allowed relations between n, l, and m_l are shown in Table 2-1.

In everyday life we are aware that two things cannot occupy the

---

[1] For wave functions that are spherically symmetric about the nucleus there is no magnetic interaction. The greater the departure from spherical symmetry, the stronger the magnetic involvement. The simplest departure is a wave function having the pattern of a figure eight with the nucleus at the center.

same place at the same time. The quantum-theoretical version of this simple idea is called the Pauli exclusion principle. It can be stated, "no two particles (such as electrons) can be in the same detailed quantum state." Of course, two electrons in entirely different atoms are considered to be in distinct states even if they have the same formal set of quantum numbers.

At first sight the Pauli principle should allow just one electron in the K shell of an atom, corresponding to the state in which $n = 1$,

Table 2-1. Relationships between the Quantum Numbers n, l, and m_l Allowed Theoretically.

Atomic shell	n	l	m_l
K	1	0	0
L	2	0	0
		1	$-1, 0, 1$
M	3	0	0
		1	$-1, 0, 1$
		2	$-2, -1, 0, 1, 2$
		$l = 0, 1, 2, \ldots, n-1$	$m_l = 0, \pm 1, \pm 2, \ldots, \pm l$

$l = 0$, $m_l = 0$. The L shell should accommodate four electrons, with $n/l/m_l$ equal to 2/0/0, 2/1/-1, 2/1/0, and 2/1/1. The M shell should provide for nine electrons in distinct states, and so forth. Actually there are twice as many distinct states: 2 in the K shell, 8 in the L shell, 18 in the M shell, and so forth. To see this we must take account of one final way in which the electron can interact with its surroundings: through the magnetic force associated with its spin.

An electron behaves like a tiny charged sphere spinning on its axis. The circulating charge gives it a magnetic moment designated by a *spin quantum number s*, equal to $\frac{1}{2}$. The axis of this spin can have either of two directions, approximately parallel or antiparallel, relative to other magnetic moments in the surroundings. These orientations are distinguished by assigning a *spin magnetic quantum number m_s*, equal to $+\frac{1}{2}$ or $-\frac{1}{2}$. Two electrons having identical values for the quantum numbers n, l, and m_l can therefore be in different states by having oppositely directed spins, $m_s = +\frac{1}{2}$ and $-\frac{1}{2}$.

We can now describe the electronic configurations of simple atoms in terms of these quantum states. The elements grow in complexity by having more protons and neutrons in the nucleus and more electrons around the nucleus. The progressive filling of the distinct states, as dictated by the Pauli principle, is reflected by the successive positions in the periodic table of the elements. This is shown in part in Table 2-2.

Table 2-2. The First Eleven Elements of the Periodic Table, Classified According to Quantum States of Their Electrons.

Element	Total	*K shell*	*L shell*	*M shell*	n	l	m_l	m_s	Designation
		Number of electrons					*Distribution among states*		
H	1	1			1	0	0	$\frac{1}{2}$	$1s$
He	2	2			1	0	0	$\frac{1}{2}, -\frac{1}{2}$	$1s^2$
Li	3	2	1		1	0	0	$\frac{1}{2}, -\frac{1}{2}$	$1s^2$
					2	0	0	$\frac{1}{2}$	$2s$
Be	4	2	2		1	0	0	$\frac{1}{2}, -\frac{1}{2}$	$1s^2$
					2	0	0	$\frac{1}{2}, -\frac{1}{2}$	$2s^2$
B	5	2	3		1	0	0	$\frac{1}{2}, -\frac{1}{2}$	$1s^2$
					2	0	0	$\frac{1}{2}, -\frac{1}{2}$	$2s^2$
					2	1	0	$\frac{1}{2}$	$2p$
C	6	2	4						
N	7	2	5				.		
O	8	2	6				.		
F	9	2	7				.		
Ne	10	2	8						
Na	11	2	8	1	1	0	0	$\frac{1}{2}, -\frac{1}{2}$	$1s^2$
					2	0	0	$\frac{1}{2}, -\frac{1}{2}$	$2s^2$
					2	1	0	$\frac{1}{2}, -\frac{1}{2}$	$2p^6$
					2	1	1	$\frac{1}{2}, -\frac{1}{2}$	$2p^6$
					2	1	-1	$\frac{1}{2}, -\frac{1}{2}$	$2p^6$
					3	0	0	$\frac{1}{2}$	$3s$

The states for which $l = 0$ are called *s* states, those for which $l = 1$ are called *p* states, and those for which $l = 2$ are called *d* states. This terminology has been crossed with a numerical designation of the total quantum number *n*, so we have the designation 2*p* for the case in which $n = 2$ and $l = 1$, and so forth. These designations are also listed in Table 2-2. If an atom has two 1*s* electrons, they are listed by a superscript: $1s^2$.

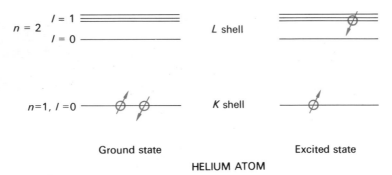

Ground state   Excited state

HELIUM ATOM

Fig. 2-8.   The state of lowest energy, or ground state, of a helium atom, and an excited state in which an electron has been promoted to the L shell. The direction of the electron spin is indicated by the arrow through each electron.

The most stable states of atoms are those in which the electrons are distributed, in accord with the Pauli principle, into the quantum states of least energy. These stable states, as listed in Table 2-2, are known as the electronic ground states. It is possible, however, for an electron to be in one of the higher states allowed by the quantum theory. For example, one of the *K*-shell electrons of helium might be promoted to the normally vacant *L* shell, as shown in Fig. 2-8. This new state is called an electronic excited state; it is produced when an atom in the ground state absorbs a quantum of suitable energy, as shown in Fig. 2-5. The left and right parts of Fig. 2-8 are represented in simpler form in Fig. 2-5 by the lower and upper horizontal lines, because these lines refer to the energy of the atom as a whole. Figure 2-5 is commonly called a transition diagram, and Fig. 2-8 an electron energy-level diagram.

2-6. *Electron Spin*

It can be seen from Table 2-2 that if a simple atom has an even number of electrons, the spins of these electrons can be grouped in oppositely directed, or antiparallel, pairs ($m_s = +\frac{1}{2}, -\frac{1}{2}$). The members of a pair then cancel each other, so the total spin moment is zero (this is often, but not always, the most stable state). With an odd number of electrons there is one spin value of $\frac{1}{2}$ left over, so the total spin is $\frac{1}{2}$ if the other spins are paired so as to cancel.

In an excited state a pair of electrons that is normally together with antiparallel spins may become divided as one electron is promoted to a higher energy level. The spin of the promoted electron may then continue to be antiparallel to that of its former partner, or it may become parallel. In the former case the total spin is zero, as in the ground state. In the latter the spin value is $\frac{1}{2} + \frac{1}{2}$ for parallel spins, or 1. This value is called the *total spin quantum number S*.

The electron spin states of atoms in some simple situations are shown in Fig. 2-9. The states $S = 0$, $S = \frac{1}{2}$, and $S = 1$ are called singlet, doublet, and triplet, respectively. This language is derived from the number of distinct ways that the spin can line up relative to an external magnetic field, as allowed by the quantum theory.[1] For $S = 1$ (triplet) three ways are allowed, one of them perpendicular to the external field. For $S = \frac{1}{2}$ (doublet) there are two ways: approximately parallel and antiparallel. For $S = 0$ there is no interaction, so all orientations of the atom in relation to the field are indistinguishable (singlet).

The energy of an atom is changed slightly when its spin interacts with an external magnetic field, and the perturbation depends on the orientations as well as on the strength of the field. A single energy state can therefore be split into two (doublet) or three (triplet) closely spaced energy states. This is shown for the doublet in Fig. 2-10. Now it is possible to cause transitions between these magnetically induced substates, by bombarding the system with quanta of the right energy.

---

[1] As with all physical parameters, the strength of interaction between magnetic moments is quantized. As a result, the magnetic moment of an atom can have only a small number of distinct orientations relative to an external magnetic moment, corresponding to a few distinct strengths of interaction.

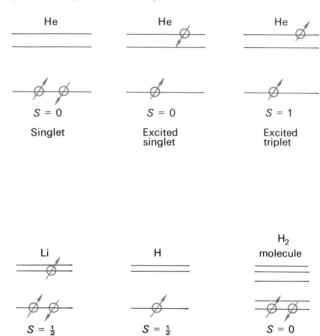

Fig. 2-9. Various electronic states for helium, lithium, and hydrogen, showing different values of the total spin quantum number S. The nomenclature of singlet, doublet, and triplet is explained in the text. Note how the atomic electron spins of hydrogen cancel in the hydrogen molecule.

These quanta are in the microwave region (wavelength about 1 cm; compare Fig. 2-3) for the magnetic field strengths that are convenient in the laboratory. This technique is extremely useful for detecting the presence of unpaired electron spins or of atoms and molecules with nonzero spin values. It is called microwave spectroscopy.

As we shall see later, the distinction between singlet and triplet states of molecules is of great importance in photochemistry and photobiology. The reason is that triplet excited states are especially long lived and reactive.

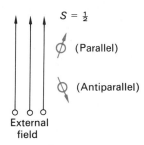

$S = \frac{1}{2}$

(Parallel)

(Antiparallel)

External
field

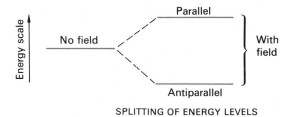

Energy scale

No field

Parallel

With
field

Antiparallel

SPLITTING OF ENERGY LEVELS

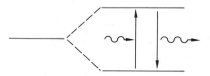

TRANSITIONS BETWEEN THE SPLIT LEVELS

Fig. 2-10. For an atom in an external magnetic field, the energy depends on the orientation of its electron spin relative to the field. For a spin value of $\frac{1}{2}$, as shown here, there are two such orientations allowed by the quantum theory. A single energy state is therefore split into two by the field. Transitions between the upper and lower of these two states can now be induced by radiation of the appropriate energy. The magnitude of the energy gap is proportional to the strength of the external field.

THE ABSORPTION AND EMISSION OF LIGHT BY MATTER

2-7. *Transitions; Rates and Equilibria*

An atom that absorbs a quantum of light is changed in two related ways: The energy of the atom is increased by an amount $h\nu$ (see Fig. 2-5), and the wave functions of the component electrons are altered in keeping with the changed state of the atom. This change in wave function during the transition from one state to another constitutes a redistribution of electric charge in the atom. One can describe such a transition in terms of classical theory by saying that the electromagnetic wave induces a dipole oscillation in the atom. This is a transitory oscillation which redistributes the electrons in relation to the nucleus and accounts for the changed wave function. During this forced oscillation, and because of it, the atom absorbs an amount of energy equal to one quantum, $h\nu$. The time needed for the entire process is of the order of one oscillation (about 10^{-15} sec for a transition induced by visible radiation). The reverse transition, from a higher to a lower energy state, can be viewed in a similar way. The change in wave function has the character of a dipole oscillation, and this oscillating dipole radiates a quantum of energy $h\nu$.

For both upward and downward transitions the dipole oscillation can be induced by an electromagnetic wave of the correct frequency. In the upward case, where energy is gained, a quantum of the inducing radiation is absorbed. The downward case involves the net emission of one quantum; we can imagine that a quantum of the inducing radiation is absorbed and reemitted, and a second quantum of the same energy is emitted as well. These processes are shown in Fig. 2-11a and b.

The downward transition can also occur spontaneously, without the help of external radiation to start the dipole oscillation. This alternative is shown in Fig. 2-5 and again in Fig. 2-11c.

The probability, per unit of time, that an atom will undergo an induced transition is proportional to the energy density of the inducing radiation field (that is, to the intensity of light of the correct frequency).

Excited state

ΔE {

Ground state

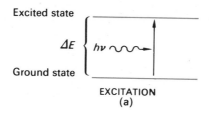

EXCITATION
(a)

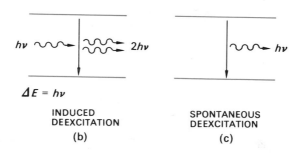

$\Delta E = h\nu$

INDUCED
DEEXCITATION
(b)

SPONTANEOUS
DEEXCITATION
(c)

Fig. 2-11. Excitation and deexcitation between the lowest energy (ground) state and a higher energy (excited) state of an atom.

The number of such transitions per second, in a collection of N atoms, can therefore be written BIN, where I is the light intensity, and B is a constant. For spontaneous downward transitions the rate is independent of light intensity and can be written AN, where A is another constant. We can now describe the equilibrium between upward and downward transitions in a collection of atoms exposed to light. Consider a set of N atoms of the same kind, each one capable of existing in either of two states: one of lower energy, the ground state, and a higher one, the excited state. Under steady illumination the ground-state and excited-state populations will reach an equilibrium such that the rates of upward and downward transitions are equal (see Fig. 2-12). Assume that in equilibrium a fraction x of the N atoms is in the excited state, leaving a fraction $1 - x$ in the ground state. Then the rate of upward transitions is $BIN(1 - x)$, while the rate of downward transitions is $BINx$ (induced) plus ANx (spontaneous).[1] Equating these rates we have

$$BIN(1 - x) = BINx + ANx \qquad (2\text{-}5)$$

which can be rearranged to give

$$x = \frac{BI}{2BI + A} \qquad (2\text{-}6)$$

for the fraction of atoms in the excited state.

Equation (2-6) shows that for a transition induced by radiation, the fraction of atoms in the excited state cannot exceed 50 percent; this limiting value is approached when $I \to \infty$. Values greater than 50 percent can only be reached by populating the excited state indirectly (by way of a third state), avoiding the use of radiation that stimulates the downward transition. If this can be done, an explosive cascade of deexcitation can then be triggered by a single quantum that stimulates the downward transition. A self-amplifying chain reaction can occur because (see Fig. 2-11b) 2 quanta are released for each one absorbed in the induced deexcitation. This is the mechanism by which a laser operates. But in most laboratory situations, as well as in nature on the earth's surface, the value of BI in Eq. (2-6) is much less than the value of A. This means that induced downward transitions are negligible in comparison with the spontaneous ones,

---

[1] The rate constant B for an induced transition depends on the difference in charge distribution between the two states. However, the symmetry of the process is such that the probability or rate constant has the same value for a transition in either direction, upward or downward.

and the fraction of atoms in the excited state is very small. With $BI \ll A$, Eq. (2-6) reduces to

$$x \approx \frac{B}{A} I \qquad (2\text{-}7)$$

The fraction x is proportional to light intensity and is much less than 1.

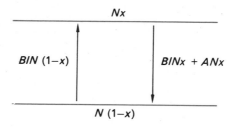

Fig. 2-12. *A set of N atoms in a radiation field of intensity I reaches a steady state with Nx atoms in the excited state and N(1 − x) in the ground state. The rate of excitations, BIN(1 − x), equals the rate of (induced plus spontaneous) deexcitations, BINx + ANx.*

Probabilities of these transitions, as expressed by the constants A and B, are governed by two factors. First, the wave functions of the ground and excited states must overlap for a transition to occur, and the probability of a transition increases with the degree of overlap. Second, the redistribution of charge during the transition (corresponding to the change in wave function) must have the character of a dipole oscillation, and the stronger this *transition dipole moment*, the more probable the transition. These factors affect A and B in the same way; the ratio of A to B is always

$$\frac{A}{B} = \frac{8\pi h \nu^3}{c^3} \qquad (2\text{-}8)$$

for a transition involving a change of energy $h\nu$.

MOLECULES

2-8. Molecular States and Orbitals

The foregoing remarks apply to complex molecules as well as to simple atoms, but the states of molecules are far more varied than those of atoms, and their description is correspondingly more complicated. The states of atoms can be described almost completely

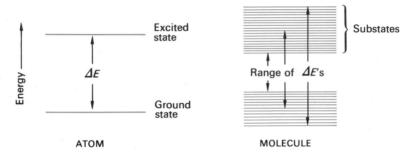

Fig. 2-13. A single state of an atom corresponds to certain distributions of the electrons. In a molecule such an electronic state is split into many substates representing different modes of vibration and rotation of nuclei and groups of nuclei. Note that the energy gap between two electronic states has a well-defined value (ΔE in the figure) for an atom, but spans a range of values in a molecule.

by specifying the "orbits" (described by wave functions) of the outermost, or valence, electrons. Such states are called electronic states; the one of least energy is the electronic ground state.

To describe a molecule one must also consider the vibrating and rotating movements of nuclei relative to the center of mass of the system. In addition there is the complication that the electrons in different atoms are brought together so that they interact with each other and with more than one nucleus, becoming components of the larger system. The result is a great proliferation of states of different energies, as shown in Fig. 2-13. One can recognize major electronic configurations, and call them electronic states ("ground" or "excited"), but each of these is subdivided into a manifold of substates reflecting finer details of interaction of the parts of the molecule.

The electronic states of molecules can be described in terms of *molecular orbitals*, analogous to the orbits in atoms. These can be visualized by drawing pictures of the wave functions of electrons in single atoms and then seeing how these might fuse to become more complicated patterns in molecules. Consider the case of two atoms sharing "$2p$" electrons (electrons for which $n = 2$ and $l = 1$). For the $2p$ electron in an individual atom, the wave function has a figure-eight pattern in which one branch has positive values of ψ and the other has negative values. Two such patterns can be brought together in many ways, two of which are shown in Fig. 2-14. In the upper of the two alignments shown, the fused wave function is an expanded version of the original one, embracing both atoms. The electrons originally associated with the individual atoms are now the common property of both, and a covalent bond has been formed. In the lower picture, in which opposite signs of ψ are adjacent, there is a plane where ψ equals zero between the atoms. This is a repulsive, or anti-bonding, configuration.

The orbitals suggested by these patterns are called π and π^*. An electron in the bonding π orbital has an energy less than in the atomic $2p$ state, and one in the π^* orbital has a greater energy. Normally the two electrons in this association occupy the π orbital; involvement of the π^* orbital represents an electronic excited state of the molecule (see Fig. 2-15). The ground state, involving only the π orbital, must be singlet because the Pauli exclusion principle requires that the spins of the two electrons be antiparallel. But the excited state, which involves π^* as well as π, can be singlet or triplet, depending on the relative spin orientations of the electrons.

The pattern of π and π^* orbitals, shown in Fig. 2-14 for two atoms, can be extended to a larger number. In benzene, the six

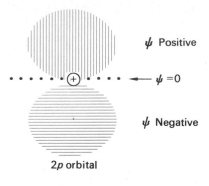

ψ Positive

ψ =0

ψ Negative

2*p* orbital

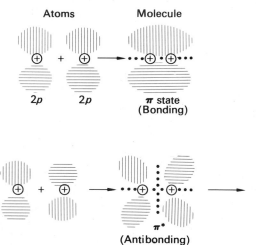

Atoms

Molecule

2*p*   2*p*

π state
(Bonding)

π*
(Antibonding)

Fig. 2-14.   *A sketch of the wave function of an atomic electron in a 2p state and of two ways in which such wave functions can fuse when the atoms are together in a molecule. Regions where ψ is positive are shaded vertically, negative regions horizontally. Planes where ψ = 0* (*zero probability of finding the electron*) *are shown by dotted lines.*

carbon atoms each contribute one $2p$ electron to a pattern that extends over all six atoms. Instead of two distinct orbitals (π and π^*) there are six, resulting from different symmetry patterns of the signs of ψ in adjacent atoms. The six electrons, in pairs with opposed

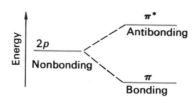

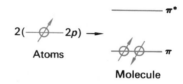

Fig. 2-15.   *When the wave functions of two 2p electrons fuse, as shown in Fig. 2-14, the resulting* π *and* π^* *orbitals represent states of lower and higher energy than the original 2p state. In the ground state both electrons are in the lower orbital, with their spins antiparallel as required by the Pauli exclusion principle.*

spins, normally occupy the three of these orbitals having the least energy (the greatest bonding character). These are then designated π, and the three higher orbitals, which are normally vacant, are called π^* (compare with the simpler case of Fig. 2-15). With three occupied and three vacant orbitals the pattern of possible transitions is complex.

The existence of an extended system of π orbitals in an organic molecule is signified by a pattern of alternating single and double bonds.

Such a set of conjugated bonds defines the extent over which the π electrons are delocalized. The more extensive the system, the more numerous and closely spaced in energy are the π and π^* orbitals. This permits transitions spanning a smaller energy gap and therefore involving quanta of light having lower frequency or greater wavelength. An example of an extensively conjugated molecule of biological importance is retinal, the pigment that is responsible for vision in higher animals:[1]

Normally the electron states of organic molecules are either vacant or filled by a pair of electrons having opposed spins, so the total spin is zero (singlet). The triplet case ($S = 1$) can arise in an excited state, as we have seen. The doublet state arises in the case of an organic radical having one unpaired electron.

2-9. *Absorption and Fluorescence Band Spectra; Excited-state Lifetime*

A transition from the ground to the excited state requires a quantum of the appropriate energy, and for an atom this energy is well defined (ΔE in Fig. 2-13). The absorption spectrum shows an intense line, or very narrow band, at the frequency or wavelength given by $h\nu = hc/\lambda = \Delta E$; this is sketched in Fig. 2-16a. In a molecule the corresponding transition can involve any of a range of quantum

---

[1] In the retina of the eye this molecule is attached to a protein molecule; the combination of retinal and protein is called rhodopsin.

energies, as indicated in Fig. 2-13. The single sharp line of the atomic absorption spectrum is replaced by a set of closely spaced lines, as shown in the right half of Fig. 2-16*b*. Each line in the spectrum pertains to a transition from a particular ground substate to a particular excited substate. The height of the line reflects the relative prob-

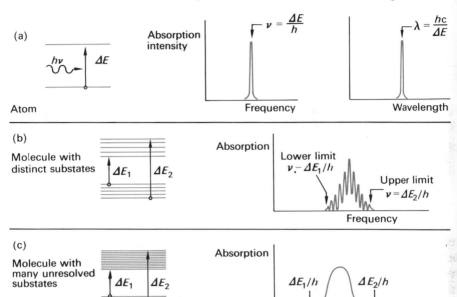

Fig. 2-16.   *Absorption spectra corresponding to an electronic transition: (a) in an atom, (b) in an idealized molecule having a few well-resolved substates, and (c) in a molecule with many unresolved substates.*

ability of that particular transition. Usually these lines, which are broadened because of interactions between the molecule and its surroundings, are so closely spaced that they cannot be resolved individually. They fuse to form a broad absorption band which describes the electronic (ground to excited) transition as a whole (Fig. 2-16*c*).

Similar remarks can be made about downward (excited to ground state) transitions and the corresponding spectra for emission of light, but in molecules the spectra of absorption and emission do not coincide. The peak of the absorption spectrum comes at a higher frequency or shorter wavelength (greater energy gap) than the peak of the emission spectrum. The same sets of energy levels are involved for both absorption and emission, but the act of absorption usually

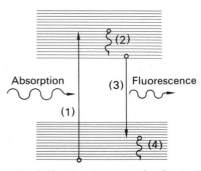

(1) Most probable
     upward transition

(2) Relaxation
     (energy exchange)
     in excited state

(3) Most probable
     downward transition

(4) Relaxation
     in ground state

Fig. 2-17. *Events in a cycle of excitation and deexcitation of a molecule. The most probable initial and final states are shown. The most probable upward transition corresponds to the peak of the absorption spectrum, and the most probable downward transition corresponds to the peak of the emission spectrum (compare Fig. 2-18).*

employs a pair of levels spanning a larger energy gap than that most commonly used in the emission act. This is shown in Fig. 2-17, which shows a cycle of light absorption and emission (fluorescence) by a molecule. First a quantum of energy is absorbed in an upward transition. Then there is an opportunity for the molecule to exchange energy with its surroundings, in a succession of small transitions between sublevels, before the downward transition. At room temperature this exchange usually puts the molecule near the bottom of the manifold of excited substates. After emission (step 3) there is another chance for energy exchange, and the molecule usually goes into one of the lower substates of the ground state.

Figure 2-17 shows only the most probable sequence of events. The act of absorption is most likely to start from a point near the bottom of the ground-state manifold, because a molecule in thermal equilibrium at room temperature will have an energy near the bottom of the manifold. The absorption will most likely terminate near the middle of the excited-state manifold, partly because the density of substates is greatest there.[1] Similar statements apply to the starting

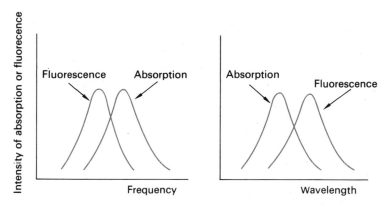

Fig. 2-18. *Spectra of absorption and fluorescence corresponding to the events depicted in Fig. 2-17.*

and ending points of the downward transitions. Actually the transitions could start anywhere in one manifold and end anywhere in the other, but with less probability for some cases than for others. The most probable events sketched in Fig. 2-17 correspond to the peaks in the spectra of absorption and emission, as shown in Fig. 2-18.

This displacement of the fluorescence spectrum relative to the absorption spectrum is called the Stokes shift. When analyzed properly, it gives information about the time available for energy

[1] There are more fundamental reasons than this, involving the Franck-Condon principle, which states that the time involved in an electronic transition is so short that the positions and momenta of the nuclei are essentially unchanged during the transition. A particular configuration of nuclei must therefore be appropriate to both the ground-state sublevel and the excited-state sublevel in order for a transition between those sublevels to occur. The transition probabilities between particular substates are therefore dictated by the availability of common nuclear configurations that link them.

exchange in the excited state, and therefore about the average time spent by a molecule in that state. Direct measurement of the lifetime is difficult. It is necessary to excite a collection of molecules with a brief flash of light and then to monitor the decline in fluorescence that reflects the declining population of excited-state molecules. The difficulty is that the decay of excitation usually occurs in about 10^{-8} sec.

Excited-state lifetimes can also be estimated from the absorption spectra of molecules. An intense absorption band signifies a highly probable upward transition. The corresponding downward transition is then also highly probable [see Eq. (2-8)], and this means in turn that the excited state is short lived. Before this relationship can be put on a useful quantitative basis, it will be necessary to develop a more precise definition of the intensity of an absorption band; this will be done in Chap. 3. For the present it can be said that the excited-state lifetime varies inversely as the intensity of absorption.

The absorption band gives a proper estimate of excited-state lifetime only if the sole avenue for deexcitation is a radiative process (fluorescence), as shown in Fig. 2-17. If other mechanisms for de-excitation are present, the lifetime will be shorter than that estimated from the absorption band. Other (nonradiative) mechanisms are indeed to be expected, and some of them are especially interesting because they involve photochemistry. A complete discussion of these matters is beyond the scope of this book, but some basic ideas can be described.

METASTABLE STATES AND PHOTOCHEMISTRY

2-10. *Allowed and Forbidden Transitions; Triplet States*

Let us first review the nature of a radiative transition. (1) The transition is induced by radiation, or is attended by the emission of a quantum of radiation. (2) The transition involves a redistribution of electric charge (a change of electronic wave functions) within the atom or molecule. (3) If this redistribution has the character of an oscillating dipole the interaction with a radiation field is strong and the transition is favored. (4) The transition is also favored if the electronic wave function in the excited state overlaps well with that in the ground state.

There are excited states for which a transition from the ground state would not involve dipole oscillation. An example is the lowest

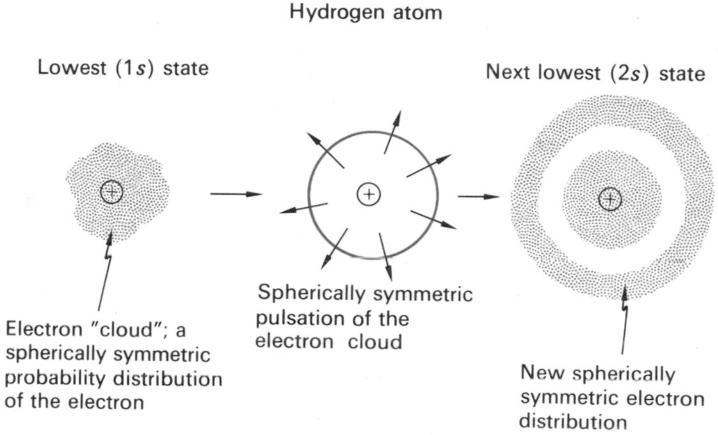

Hydrogen atom

Lowest (1*s*) state   Next lowest (2*s*) state

Electron "cloud"; a spherically symmetric probability distribution of the electron

Spherically symmetric pulsation of the electron cloud

New spherically symmetric electron distribution

Fig. 2-19. An example of a "forbidden" transition. An electromagnetic wave cannot induce the spherically symmetric pulsation of charge that would be required for this kind of transition.

excited state (the 2*s* state; $n = 2$ and $l = 0$) of a hydrogen atom. To reach this state from the ground (1*s*) state, the atom would need to perform a spherically symmetric pulsation of its electron distribution, as sketched in Fig. 2-19. This transition cannot be induced by radiation; it is "forbidden." The upper state can, however, be reached through a still higher state in two consecutive radiative ("allowed") transitions, as shown in Fig. 2-20. In this figure the upper state is labeled "metastable." Once an atom has entered this state it cannot return to the ground state without an input of energy which will carry it again through a higher excited state.

In molecules the transitions between states cannot be defined so purely in terms of allowedness or forbiddenness. For one thing, the symmetries of the various states are continually spoiled by collisions between molecules, and even by distortions due to relative movements of different parts of a single molecule. Nevertheless, there are some transitions that are predominantly allowed and others that are relatively forbidden. The π-π^* transitions described earlier

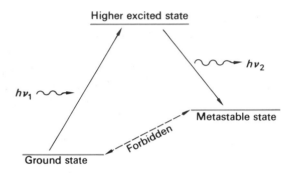

Fig. 2-20.   A means of entering a state for which a direct transition from the ground state is forbidden. Such a state is metastable; a return to the ground state must involve another passage through a higher excited state.

are strongly favored, both because there is a strong dipole character to the change from π to π^* and because the π and π^* wave functions overlap well in space. Transitions of this kind account for practically all the intense bands in the absorption spectra of molecules, and for those cases in which fluorescence is easy to observe. Because of the high transition probability, the excited state lasts only about 10^{-8} sec or less. We will use the term "allowed" loosely to categorize these more probable transitions.

The foregoing has referred specifically to the π-π^* transitions that produce singlet excited states from singlet ground states: The directions of electron spins do not change during excitation. If the spin of the promoted electron should be reversed, becoming more or less parallel to that of its former partner, the result would be a triplet excited state. This spin reversal is generally unlikely, because the radiation that causes the transition interacts only weakly with the magnetic force of the spin. Therefore, a transition from singlet to triplet, or vice versa, is relatively forbidden, and a triplet excited state obtained from a singlet ground state is metastable. The singlet-triplet transition is usually so improbable that it does not produce a measurable absorption band. The triplet excited state, once formed,

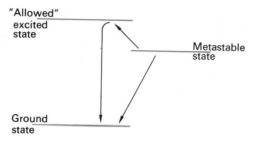

Fig. 2-21.   *Alternative paths for the return from a metastable state to the ground state. In this context "allowed" means that a radiative transition between the excited state and the ground state is favored (see the text). The transition from metastable to ground is shown here to be weakly allowed rather than strictly forbidden.*

usually has a lifetime in the range of 10^{-4} to 10^{-1} sec, about a million times that of the singlet excited state. Such states can nevertheless be produced with high yield through indirect paths of the sort indicated in Fig. 2-20. The return to the ground state may then retrace the indirect path or it may be direct; the alternatives are sketched in Fig. 2-21.

Even by an indirect path, a change of spin orientation must occur at some point if a singlet state is to be converted to a triplet, or vice versa. The spin is encouraged to change by factors that remove the electron from proximity to its opposed-spin partner and bring it under the influence of other magnetic forces in its surroundings. Such factors are (1) excitation, if the excited electron orbital is more spread out in space; (2) collisions that spoil the symmetry of perfectly opposed magnetic moments and thereby expose new magnetic forces; and (3) the magnetic field of a heavy atomic nucleus. If these factors are especially favorable, as in the mercury atom, some singlet-triplet transitions become as probable as the so-called allowed transitions.

2-11. Types of Light Emission

We are now in a position to make a useful classification of light emission into three types: fluorescence, delayed fluorescence, and phosphorescence. Imagine that a flash of light, applied to a collection of molecules, has produced certain populations of excited states. These populations will decay to the ground state, emitting light as they do so. In the simplest case we deal only with allowed transitions and observe only the fast-decaying (about 10^{-8} sec) fluorescence as indicated in Figs. 2-5, 2-17, and 2-22a. But if a metastable state is added to the system, two new kinds of emission can be expected, corresponding to the two decay routes of Fig. 2-21. The first (by the indirect route) is a delayed fluorescence. After a sojourn in the metastable state a molecule can return to the primary excited state and then to ground, emitting a "delayed" fluorescent quantum (Fig. 2-22b). This delayed fluorescence has the same spectrum (same energy gap) as ordinary fluorescence, but a much slower decay as befits the greater lifetime of the metastable state that feeds the process. Finally one can observe emission attending a direct return from metastable to ground (Fig. 2-22c). This emission shows the same slow decay as delayed fluorescence, being governed by the metastable-state population. However, its spectrum is shifted toward lower frequencies or greater wavelengths, since the energy gap, from metastable to ground, is less than that involved in fluorescence. Thus, by studying both the lifetime and the spectrum of emitted light, one can learn something about the nature and the fate of the excited-state populations. Analysis of emitted light is one of the chief tools of photochemists and photobiologists.

Because of their long lifetimes, the metastable states (usually triplet states) of molecules often serve as starting points for photochemical processes.

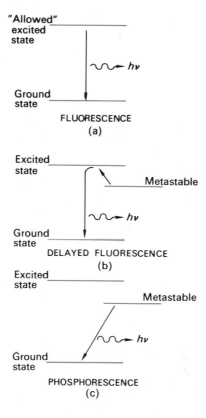

Fig. 2-22.   Three kinds of light emission.
Delayed fluorescence has the same spectrum (involving the same energy gap) as
fluorescence but a much greater lifetime.
Phosphorescence has the greater lifetime
characteristic of the metastable state and
its spectrum is shifted to greater wavelengths (smaller energy gap).

2-12. *Photochemical Catalysis in General*

By definition a photochemical process is a light-dependent chemical process. This usually means that a chemical process is initiated by a substance in an electronic excited state, produced directly (Fig. 2-17) or indirectly (Fig. 2-20) by light. In general, a chemical process can be described as follows (see Fig. 2-23). Substances or groups of substances A and B are interconverted by way of an intermediate state $\widehat{AB}$. If the energy of $\widehat{AB}$ is greater than that of either A or B,

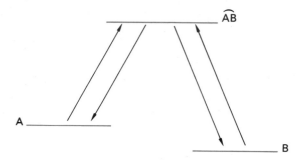

Fig. 2-23.   *Energy diagram of a reversible chemical process involving reactants and products A and B and an intermediate state $\widehat{AB}$.*

then both A and B are reasonably stable. The rate of conversion from A to B is governed mainly by the energy barrier between A and $\widehat{AB}$; this *activation energy* must be supplied, in a dark chemical process, by a random fluctuation in the pattern of thermal equilibrium. The higher the temperature, the greater the chance that a suitably large fluctuation will occur. The reverse process, B to A, is governed similarly by the energy gap between B and $\widehat{AB}$. Another factor in these processes is the relative likelihood that $\widehat{AB}$, once formed, will decay either to A or to B. For a reversible process the final equilibrium is dictated by the relative rates of the four events shown by arrows in Fig. 2-23. It can be shown that this equilibrium depends on the difference in energy between A and B, but not on the energy of $\widehat{AB}$.

Thus the activation barrier controls the reaction rates but not the ultimate ratio of A to B. The state of lower energy, B in Fig. 2-23, is favored in the final equilibrium. Quantitative formulation of these ideas is in the province of elementary thermodynamics.

A catalyst (in biology, an enzyme) has the property of lowering the energy of the intermediate state and thus speeding the chemical processes, as indicated in Fig. 2-24a. Some photochemical processes, on the other hand, provide a special mechanism by which the high energy of $\widehat{AB}$ can be reached. The energy is provided by a quantum of light rather than by a chance excursion from thermal equilibrium. The rate of the process is then governed by the intensity and wavelength of the light and not primarily by the temperature. An example is shown in Fig. 2-24b. Light excites A to an excited state A*, which can be converted to $\widehat{AB}$ and thence to either A or B. In this example A is the only light-absorbing substance. The reaction is consequently driven preferentially from A to B, and this would be so even if the energy of B were greater than that of A. A more general version of Fig. 2-24b would include an excited state B*, with processes $B \rightarrow B^* \rightarrow \widehat{AB}$ as well as $A \rightarrow A^* \rightarrow \widehat{AB}$. Light could then drive the system in both directions ($A \rightarrow B$ and $B \rightarrow A$) simultaneously. The ratio of A to B would have one equilibrium value in the dark and another during prolonged steady illumination. The latter situation is known as a photostationary state.

2-13. *Photochemical Electron Transfer*

The basic picture of Fig. 2-24b can be modified in many ways to describe particular kinds of photochemistry. One example is photochemical oxidoreduction,[1] in which a light-absorbing molecule (the sensitizer) mediates the transfer of an electron from one molecule (the donor) to another (the acceptor). To describe this, we must keep track of the movements of electrons, so we will use electron energy-level diagrams (see Fig. 2-8). The change from ground to

---

[1] An elementary description of chemical oxidation and reduction is made in sec. 4-1, vol. II.

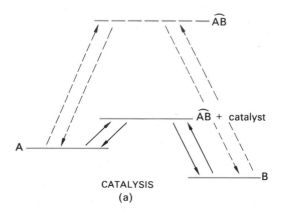

CATALYSIS
(a)

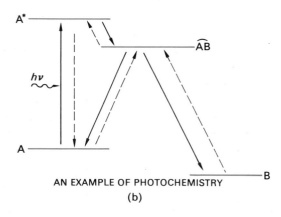

AN EXAMPLE OF PHOTOCHEMISTRY
(b)

Fig. 2-24. The reaction system of Fig. 2-23 can be sped up by a catalyst or by a photochemical process. In the example of photochemistry shown here, the reaction is driven preferentially toward the formation of B. Slower processes are indicated by dashed arrows.

excited state can be visualized as being mainly the promotion of a single electron in the molecule to an orbital[1] of higher energy, with a vacancy appearing in the lower-energy orbital, as indicated in Fig. 2-25. Two simplifications have been introduced in this and the next two figures. First, the second electron in the ground-state orbital (the partner with opposite spin) has been left out. Second, the energy levels shift slightly depending on their state of occupancy, and this is not shown.

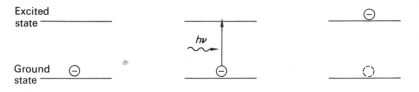

MOLECULE IN GROUND STATE   UPWARD TRANSITION   MOLECULE IN EXCITED STATE

Fig. 2-25.   The ground and excited states of molecules can be described further by showing the promotion of an electron in the molecule. This is an oversimplification because excitation redistributes all the parts of a molecule, not just one electron.

Photochemical electron transfer can now be portrayed as in Fig. 2-26. Initially the donor D, the sensitizer S, and the acceptor A are all in their ground states (Fig. 2-26a). The ground- and excited-state energies of the donor are greater than their counterparts in the sensitizer, and the states of the sensitizer are in turn higher than those of the acceptor. The sensitizer absorbs a quantum (Fig. 2-26a) and enters the excited state, leaving an electron vacancy in the ground state (Fig. 2-26b). At this point the electron could fall back into its ground-state orbital and restore the *status ante* of Fig. 2-26a. Alternatively, the excited electron could enter the vacant higher orbital of the acceptor. Meanwhile the vacancy in the ground state of the sensitizer could be filled by an electron from the donor. These electron

[1] It should be emphasized again that an orbital or orbit in the usual sense is not a proper concept because of the uncertainty principle. The term is used here as a convenient way to refer to the wave function, or probability distribution map, of the electron.

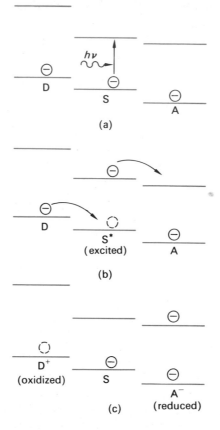

Fig. 2-26.   A sensitizing pigment S can mediate the photochemical transfer of an electron from a donor molecule D to an acceptor molecule A.

displacements are shown by the arrows in Fig. 2-26*b*. The end result would be the creation of two new species: reduced acceptor A^- and oxidized donor D^+, as shown in Fig. 2-26*c*. The sensitizer is restored to its original ground state; it thus functions catalytically.

The two electron transfer steps shown by the arrows in Fig. 2-26*b* need not occur simultaneously. If the right-hand event (electron from S* to A) occurred earlier, oxidized sensitizer would be identified as a transitory substance in the reaction. If the left-hand event took

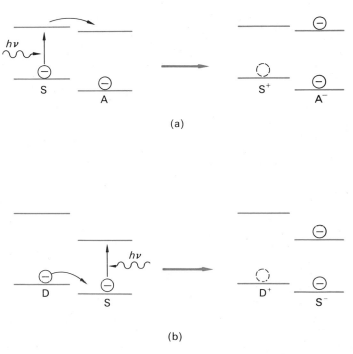

(a)

(b)

Fig. 2-27. Photochemical oxidation or reduction of the sensitizer; a partial reaction of the more complete system shown in Fig. 2-26.

place earlier, there would be a temporary presence of reduced sensitizer. These partial processes and products can sometimes be demonstrated by omitting either the donor or the acceptor from the reaction mixture. In that case one can obtain oxidized or reduced sensitizer as a stable product of the reaction (Fig. 2-27).

Obviously the central activity of photochemists and photobiologists is to characterize the products of photochemical reactions and to elucidate the detailed mechanisms by which these products are formed.

DEEXCITATION PROCESSES

2-14. Thermal Relaxation

When a molecule makes a transition from one energy state to another, it necessarily loses or gains energy to or from its surroundings. In radiative processes this energy is recognized as an absorbed or emitted quantum. In a cycle of radiative excitation and deexcitation there is often a discrepancy between the energies of the absorbed and emitted quanta (see Fig. 2-17), but this discrepancy is explained in terms of energy exchange. The relaxation steps, (2) and (4) in Fig. 2-17, comprise many transitions between substates, and in each of these small downward transitions a small quantum of energy is given to the surroundings. These quanta lie far below the domain of visible light and are perceived only as heat.

Between the sets of excited and ground substates there is usually a gap (E_1 in Fig. 2-16c) in which substates are sparse or seemingly absent. If this gap is to be crossed at one jump, in a downward transition, an appropriately large quantum must be emitted. If such a quantum is not observed as fluorescence we should seek an explanation. Sometimes the explanation involves a cascade through substates. The excited and ground electronic states might be connected smoothly by overlapping of their substates, as shown in Fig. 2-28, allowing energy to be given up in small increments. Such a system might also allow a variety of low-energy upward transitions, giving an appreciable "tail" on the long-wave side of the absorption band, but in actuality this is rarely seen. Alternatively the cascade might utilize metastable (triplet) substates, as suggested in Fig. 2-29. A proper formulation of this problem involves a mixing of different ground and excited substates having the same nuclear configurations and is beyond the scope of this book.

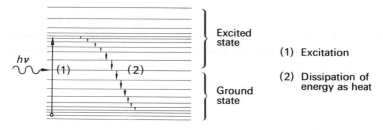

Excited
state

(1) Excitation

Ground
state

(2) Dissipation of
energy as heat

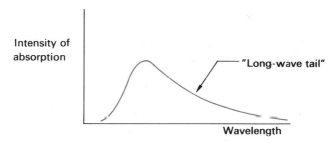

Intensity of
absorption

"Long-wave tail"

Wavelength

*Fig. 2-28.   A hypothetical molecule in which fluorescence is suppressed because
the sublevels of the excited and ground states overlap. The absorption spectrum
of such a molecule should show an appreciable "tail" at greater wavelengths.*

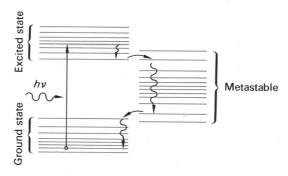

*Fig. 2-29.   A model for radiationless deexcitation in
which energy is dissipated through metastable substates.*

Often the absence of fluorescence is explained readily in terms of a photochemical process. In the events shown in Fig. 2-26, the energy of the excited sensitizer molecule is given to the acceptor molecule at one stroke in the form of a high-energy electron. The sensitizer gains a lower-energy electron from the donor and thus returns to its

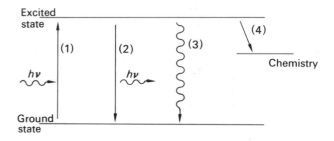

(1) Absorption

(2) Fluorescence

(3) Radiationless deexcitation

(4) Photochemistry

Fig. 2-30.   Showing various fates (pathways of deexcitation) of a molecule in an excited state. The radiationless and photochemical pathways might involve metastable states as intermediates.

normal ground state. Figure 2-30 shows the possibility of three avenues of deexcitation: fluorescence, photochemistry (of some specified kind), and radiationless deexcitation. In this figure, as in many earlier and subsequent ones, the sublevels of ground and excited states have been omitted for simplicity.

The absorption spectra of most molecules show two or more bands, indicating that there are two or more distinct electronic excited states (Fig. 2-31). Usually such molecules exhibit fluorescence only from the lower excited state, as indicated in Fig. 2-32. The explanation here is straightforward. The two excited states are well connected through their substates; this is attested by the way that the tails of the two absorption bands overlap each other. There is thus a good avenue for radiationless decay from the higher to the

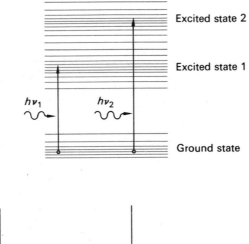

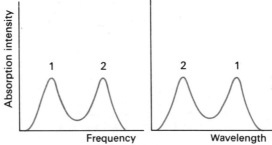

Fig. 2-31.　*Absorption spectra of a molecule showing two electronic excited states.*

lower of the excited states through consecutive small transitions among substates. This process of heat dissipation proceeds so rapidly (in about 10^{-12} sec) that it supervenes over any other fate of the higher excited state. For most purposes it is therefore immaterial whether the molecule is excited into the higher or the lower excited state. The higher state is converted to the lower before anything else

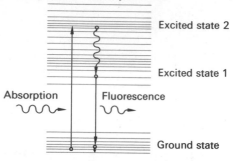

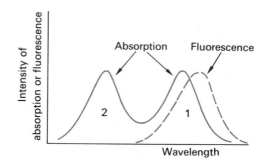

Fig. 2-32. *Deexcitation in a molecule with two excited states. Excitation into the higher excited state leads to a rapid radiationless decay to the lower excited state, followed by a fluorescent return to the ground state.*

(such as fluorescence or photochemistry) can happen, so the more energetic quanta that excite the higher state are of no greater use than the weaker quanta that can excite only the lower state. There are as yet no convincing exceptions to this rule in photobiology.

2-15. Competitive Processes and the Quantum Yield of Fluorescence

Returning to Fig. 2-30, the three downward processes shown are all contributing competitively to the decay of the excited-state population. An increase in the rate of any one of these processes would cause it to assume a greater share of the decay process and would shorten the average lifetime of the excited state. These relationships are best expressed mathematically. Let n be the number of molecules in the excited state. The rate of deexcitation is proportional to the number of excited molecules, and each kind of process has its own rate constant:

Fluorescent deexcitations per second $= k_f n$
Radiationless deexcitations per second $= k_d n$
Photochemical deexcitations per second $= k_p n$
Total deexcitations per second $= (k_f + k_d + k_p)n$

In a steady state, under constant illumination, the rate of deexcitation is balanced by an equal rate of excitation so that n assumes a constant value.

The quantum yield of fluorescence ϕ_f can now be defined as the number of fluorescent quanta divided by the number of quanta absorbed. In a steady state this is the same as the rate of fluorescent deexcitation divided by the rate of total deexcitation (or excitation). Thus

$$\phi_f = \frac{k_f n}{(k_f + k_d + k_p)n}$$

or

$$\phi_f = \frac{k_f}{k_f + k_d + k_p} \qquad (2\text{-}9)$$

That is, the yield of fluorescence is given by the rate constant for fluorescence divided by the sum of the rate constants for all competing processes of deexcitation.

2-16. Kinetics: Excited-state Lifetime and Fluorescence Yield

Now consider the case where the exciting light is turned off suddenly. Let n_0 be the number of excited molecules at the instant the light is turned off, and n be the number at some later time. This number decreases at a rate $-dn/dt$, equal to the rate of deexcitation:

$$\frac{-dn}{dt} = (k_f + k_d + k_p)n \qquad (2\text{-}10)$$

This can be written

$$\frac{dn}{n} = -k \, dt$$

where $k = k_f + k_d + k_p$. Integrating both sides gives

$$\ln n = kt + \text{const}$$

and since $n = n_0$ when $t = 0$,

$$\ln n_0 = \text{const}$$

Combining these expressions, we have

$$\ln n = -kt + \ln n_0$$

or

$$n = n_0 e^{-kt} \tag{2-11}$$

The excitation decays exponentially with time, falling to $1/e$ of its initial value when $kt = 1$, or when $t = 1/k$. This "average" lifetime is written τ:

$$\tau = \frac{1}{k} = \frac{1}{k_f + k_d + k_p} \tag{2-12}$$

Comparing Eqs. (2-9) and (2-12), we see that

$$\phi_f = k_f \tau \tag{2-13}$$

The yield of fluorescence is proportional to the mean lifetime of the excited state. If the processes competing with fluorescence could be eliminated, k_d and k_p would be zero. Then ϕ_f would equal 100 percent [see Eq. (2-9)] and τ would have its greatest possible value,

$$\tau_0 = \frac{1}{k_f} \tag{2-14}$$

as is evident from Eq. (2-12). This greatest value τ_0 is called the intrinsic lifetime of the excited state; it is the lifetime that would prevail if fluorescence were the only avenue for return to the ground state. Combining Eqs. (2-13) and (2-14), we have

$$\phi_f = \frac{\tau}{\tau_0} \tag{2-15}$$

Thus the (actual) yield of fluorescence equals the actual lifetime divided by the intrinsic lifetime of the excited state.

In an earlier section it was stated that the lifetime of an excited state varies inversely as the intensity of absorption. This statement is correct only for the intrinsic lifetime. When properly applied in conjunction with Eqs. (2-15) and (3-17) (see later), it affords a three-way comparison among the intensity of absorption, the yield of fluorescence, and the actual lifetime. Any one of these parameters can be computed from the other two.

The application of these relationships will be examined later in connection with actual photobiological problems. First we will have to develop our theory in more practical terms; this will be done in Chap. 3. In particular we will formulate concrete and precise definitions for the quantity of light and the intensity of light absorption by molecules.

TRANSFER OF EXCITATION ENERGY

2-17. Demonstrations and Descriptions of Energy Transfer

Consider a dye A having two intense absorption bands, one in the blue part of the spectrum and one in the red. Now suppose that a second dye B has just one band, at wavelengths a little beyond the red band of A, as shown in Fig. 2-33a. The fluorescence band of B is at still greater wavelengths. Now if these dyes are together in a concentrated solution, say one-tenth molar, and blue light is put in, we can sometimes observe the fluorescence characteristic of B. The use

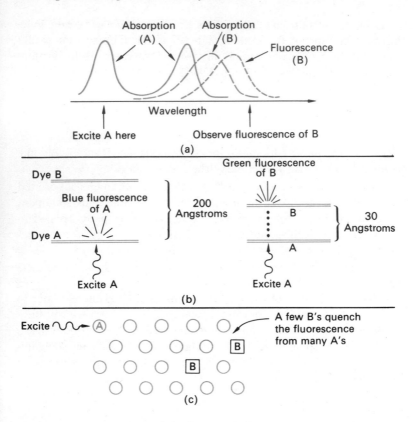

Fig. 2-33.   *Three experiments showing the transfer of excitation energy from a dye A to a second dye B.*

of blue light assures us that the energy of excitation was absorbed exclusively by A. Emission of fluorescence by B then shows that the excited state was somehow transferred from A to B. If the solution is made more dilute, the efficiency of this energy transfer diminishes and the fluorescence of B is replaced by direct fluorescence from A.

The same thing was shown in an elegant way by Hans Kuhn, who employed very thin layers of dyes, one or two molecules thick but many square centimeters in area. These layers were made into sandwiches: dye A and dye B were separated a known distance by layers of a fatty acid. Then if the layers were close enough together, excitation of A produced fluorescence from B, as shown in Fig. 2-33*b*.

The efficiency of this energy transfer depends both on the distance between A and B and on how nicely the fluorescence band of A (not shown in the figure) overlaps with the long-wave absorption band of B. For good overlap the efficiency of transfer can exceed 90 percent when A and B are within about 30 Å of each other (recall that 1 Å equals 10^{-8} cm). This efficiency is so great that we must rule out the trivial explanation that dye A emits a quantum of fluorescence which is then absorbed by B, followed by fluorescence of B. The transfer involves a coordinated process in which the excitation of B is coupled closely with the deexcitation of A, as sketched in Fig. 2-34.

Efficient energy transfer can also take place among molecules of the same kind, as shown by the experiment illustrated in Fig. 2-33*c*. We have many molecules of substance A capable of absorbing light and emitting fluorescence. Now suppose that substance B acts as a quencher: Any energy transferred to it is dissipated rapidly in radiationless deexcitations. It may then be observed that a few molecules of B, added to an aggregate of many molecules of A, are able to quench the fluorescence of A almost entirely. The quenching effect of B may be exerted over such large distances in the aggregate that a direct transfer, from each excited A to the nearest quencher, must be ruled out as the mechanism. We must then suppose that the transfer is facilitated by a migration of the excitation energy from one molecule of A to another. This "random walk" of the energy through the aggregate continues until eventually the quantum of excitation encounters a molecule of B and the energy is dissipated. This kind of "homogeneous" energy transfer is best studied in organic crystals, where the individual molecules are close to each other and spaced regularly. However, a different formalism is more appropriate for this case. Rather than describing a random walk resulting from pairwise transfer between molecules, it is more correct and fruitful to consider the aggregate of A's as a "supermolecule." The energy of excitation then exists as an excited state of this supermolecule. It

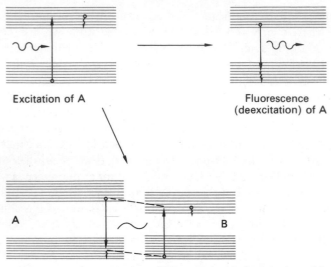

Excitation of A

Fluorescence
(deexcitation) of A

Energy transfer: excitation of B coupled with deexcitation of A

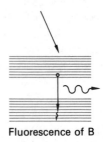

Fluorescence of B

*Fig. 2-34.   Excitation of dye A might lead either to fluorescence of
A or to transfer of the energy to B, as indicated:*

is a property of the aggregate, and is effectively delocalized throughout
the entire set of molecules. Of course, in the process of quenching
by a molecule of B the energy ceases to be associated with the whole
aggregate; it becomes localized in B.

   This transfer of energy is of the greatest importance in photosynthesis, where many molecules of chlorophyll act collectively as a

light-harvesting unit, analogous to the aggregate of A's. The absorbed light energy is then transferred to sites (analogous to the B's) where it is utilized for photochemistry.

BIBLIOGRAPHY

More advanced material is indicated by an asterisk.

1. Gamow, G.: "Mr. Tompkins in Wonderland," The Macmillan Company, New York, 1946. Fantasy illustrating principles of modern physics.
2. *Sci. Am.*, vol. 219, no. 3, September, 1968. An entire issue on the subject of light.
3. Clayton, R. K.: "Molecular Physics in Photosynthesis," Blaisdell Publishing Company, a division of Ginn and Company, Waltham, Mass., 1965. Includes a descriptive treatment of molecular physics, radiation physics, and some aspects of photochemistry and photobiology.
4. Seliger, H. H. and W. D. McElroy: "Light: Physical and Biological Action," Academic Press, Inc., New York, 1965. A general treatment of physical photobiology.
5. Reid, C.: "Excited States in Chemistry and Biology," Academic Press, Inc., New York, 1957. A concise but quite sophisticated account of molecular excitation.
6. Augenstine, L. G. (ed.): Bioenergetics, *Radiation Res.*, Supplement 2. Academic Press, Inc., New York, 1960. Articles on aspects of light and matter. See especially contributions by M. Kasha, p. 243 (molecular orbitals and other topics), S. P. McGlynn, p. 300 (electron transfer in the excited state), and T. Förster, p. 326 (intermolecular transfer of excitation energy).
*7. Rice, F. O., and E. Teller: "The Structure of Matter," John Wiley and Sons, Inc., New York, 1949. An excellent semi-descriptive account of the physics of atoms and molecules.
*8. Pauling, L.: "The Nature of the Chemical Bond," 3d ed., Cornell University Press, Ithaca, N.Y., 1960. The definitive treatment of valence and chemical structure.

*9. Gurney, R. W.: "Elementary Quantum Mechanics," Cambridge University Press, London and New York, 1940. A relatively simple introduction to the subject.

*10. Kompaneyets, A. S.: "Basic Concepts in Quantum Mechanics," translation ed., L. F. Landovitz. Reinhold Publishing Corporation, New York, 1966. From the Russian, a fine semidescriptive introduction to quantum mechanics.

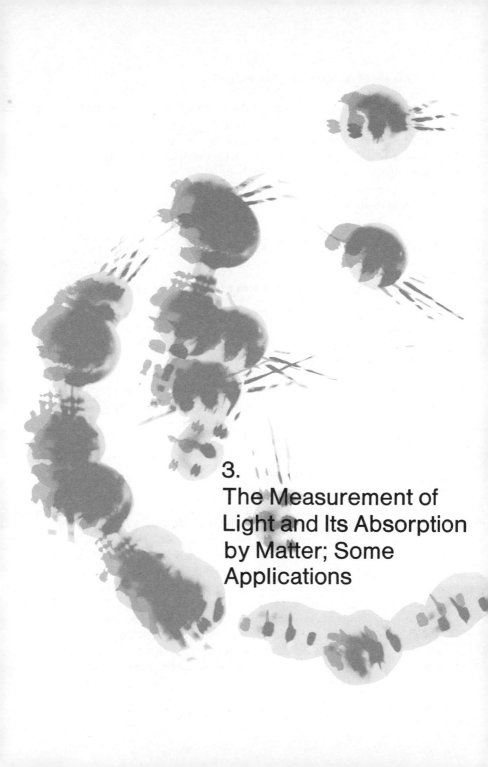

3.
The Measurement of
Light and Its Absorption
by Matter; Some
Applications

Having examined some aspects of the nature of light and matter, we will turn in this chapter to more practical considerations: to the quantitative measurement of light and to the uses of such measurements in studying the interactions between light and matter. Some details of the methods for producing, detecting, and characterizing light can be found in the appendixes. For the present we will assume that these methods exist and will deal mainly with the theory.

QUANTITY AND INTENSITY OF LIGHT

3-1. *Physical Units of the Quantity and Intensity of Light*

Light is a form of energy, and it is natural to express its quantity in energy units such as ergs, joules, or calories. Because light is quantized, it is just as natural to state the number of quanta. In either case a complete description requires that the wavelength or frequency be given, and the units can then be interconverted through the relation $E = h\nu = hc/\lambda$. As an example let us compute the energy of a single quantum of wavelength 600 nm (6×10^{-5} cm). Planck's constant is 6.6×10^{-27} erg cm and the speed of light is 3×10^{10} cm/sec, so the energy in ergs is

$$E = \frac{hc}{\lambda} = \frac{(6.6 \times 10^{-27} \text{ erg sec}) (3 \times 10^{10} \text{ cm sec}^{-1})}{6 \times 10^{-5} \text{ cm}} = 3.3 \times 10^{-12} \text{ erg}$$

In practice we often deal with light made up of a mixture of wavelengths (white or *broad-band colored* light), and this complicates any calculations such as the foregoing which involve wavelength. The mixture must be analyzed so that the light in each narrow interval of wavelength $d\lambda$ can be treated separately (see Fig. 3-1). The separate contributions can then be pooled or summed in whatever way is appropriate. Under field conditions, involving daylight, these complications cannot be avoided. In the laboratory it is desirable and often essential to use monochromatic light, such that the wavelength can be treated as a single well-defined number. For example, an emission spectrum like the one suggested in Fig. 3-1 could not be measured without sampling successive narrow wavelength intervals by means of a monochromator.[1]

The energy of light might be expressed in ergs, joules (1 joule = 10^7 ergs), calories (1 cal = 4.185 joules), or electron volts (1 ev = 1.6×10^{-12} erg). One electron volt is the energy gained by an electron

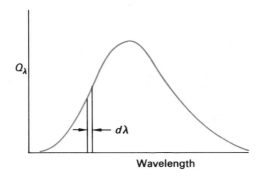

Fig. 3-1. *Most sources of light emit a mixture of wavelengths. This can be described by an emission spectrum, showing the amount of light emitted in each narrow band of wavelength ($d\lambda$) as a function of wavelength. Q_λ is the amount of light emitted per unit of increment in the wavelength. The light in the interval $d\lambda$ is then equal to $Q_\lambda d\lambda$, and the total light is the sum of these contributions: $Q_{total} = \int Q_\lambda d\lambda$. This sum is the area under the curve.*

when it is accelerated through a difference in electric potential of one volt. This is the energy scale used by chemists to describe oxidation-reduction processes; a chemical potential of one volt signifies an energy of one electron volt per molecule.

Numerical conversion between these units is shown in Table 3-1, where the wavelength λ is to be expressed in nanometers.

[1] A monochromator is a device for selecting light of a given wavelength out of a mixture of wavelengths. It uses either a prism or a diffraction grating to spread a narrow line of white light into a spectrum. See any book on optics.

In photochemistry we measure reactants and products in gram-moles, and it is useful to measure light correspondingly. Just as one mole of a substance equals 6×10^{23} (Avogadro's number) molecules, one mole of light can be defined as 6×10^{23} quanta. This amount of light is called one einstein. If a photochemical process requires one quantum per molecule of product, it requires one einstein per mole of product. The relations between einsteins and ergs or calories are included in Table 3-1.

Table 3-1.   Conversion Factors for the Energy of Light.

The energy of one quantum is

$$\frac{2 \times 10^{-9}}{\lambda} \text{ erg,} \qquad \frac{2 \times 10^{-16}}{\lambda} \text{ joule,}$$

$$\frac{0.48 \times 10^{-16}}{\lambda} \text{ cal,} \qquad \text{or} \qquad \frac{1{,}240}{\lambda} \text{ ev}$$

The energy of one einstein (one mole of quanta) is

$$\frac{12 \times 10^{14}}{\lambda} \text{ ergs} \qquad \text{or} \qquad \frac{285 \times 10^5}{\lambda} \text{ cal}$$

In these formulas the wavelength λ is to be expressed in nanometers

Although we have been discussing quantity of light, we usually deal with the rate at which light is being generated, transmitted, or absorbed. A household lamp, for example, radiates energy at a *rate* of so many watts (one watt is one joule per second; it is a unit of power rather than energy). Imagine that a lamp is fitted with a lens that converts some of the light into a uniform parallel beam, as shown in Fig. 3-2. Consider an area S perpendicular to the beam. Of the total power radiated by the lamp, some part P (watts) passes through this area. The *intensity* of light in the beam can now be defined as the power per unit of cross section:

$$\text{Intensity } I \text{ (watts/cm}^2) = \frac{P \text{ (watts)}}{S \text{ (cm}^2)} \qquad (3\text{-}1)$$

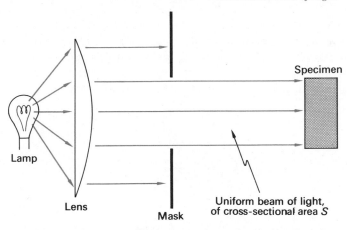

Fig. 3-2. A common configuration in the study of photochemistry.

If the surface S represents the boundary of a system being studied, energy enters the system at a rate P equal to the intensity I multiplied by the area S. The system might be a section of a leaf, or a region of skin surface, or a vessel containing a photochemical system in solution.

In this discussion the intensity has been defined in terms of energy, but the definition could have been framed in terms of quanta or moles of quanta. From Table 3-1 it is easy to derive the conversions shown in Table 3-2.

Table 3-2. Conversions for Light Intensity in Various Units. The Wavelength Must Be Expressed in Nanometers.

$$1 \text{ einstein/cm}^2 \text{ sec} = \frac{12 \times 10^{14}}{\lambda} \text{ ergs/cm}^2 \text{ sec} = \frac{12 \times 10^7}{\lambda} \text{ watts/cm}^2$$

$$1 \text{ watt/cm}^2 \qquad = 10^7 \text{ ergs/cm}^2 \text{ sec} \qquad = 8.3 \times 10^{-9} \, (\lambda) \text{ einstein/cm}^2 \text{ sec}$$

3-2. Subjective Units

The foregoing physical units of light quantity and light intensity are to be preferred for most purposes in photochemistry and photobiology. There is another class of units, well established in the litera-

ture on optics, that is based on the appearance of brightness as seen
by humans. It includes the candle, the lumen, the foot candle, and so
forth. To understand these units, we need to recognize that within
the visible spectrum certain wavelengths are "more visible" than
others; an approximate plot of relative visibility versus wavelength

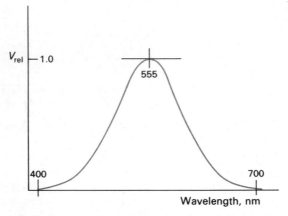

*Fig. 3-3.   The relative visibility V_{rel} of light of wavelength
λ as seen by the light-adapted human eye. Green light,
555 nm, is the most visible (50 candles/watt); the visibility
approaches zero at 400 and 700 nm. This curve defines the
visible spectrum.*

for the light-adapted human eye is shown in Fig. 3-3. Green light of
wavelength 555 nm is the most visible, and the visibility declines
toward zero at the extremes of the violet and the red (400 and 700 nm).
This curve is related closely to the ability of pigments in the eye to
absorb light.

A source of light has a luminosity of one candle if its output
appears to match that of a "standard candle." Originally this was an
actual candle made in a prescribed way; now the candle is based on
the average of 45 standard carbon filament lamps kept at the National
Bureau of Standards (U.S.), operated at a specified current. Since
this unit involves a judgment of brightness, its calibration implies

not only a standard source but also a standard observer. The standard observer is one whose visibility curve matches an accepted curve based on the average for many observers.

A light source of one candle (or candlepower) has approximately the brightness of a common household candle.

The visibility curve implies that human subjects have been asked to make a "brightness match" for two fields of different colors, such as red and green; one may wonder how reliable a subjective decision of this kind can be. Probably the best justification for the procedure is that the curve obtained in this way matches closely the absorption spectrum of the mixture of cone pigments in the eye (cones are the light-sensitive cells that mediate vision under conditions of adaptation to bright light).

A source of monochromatic light, such as the output of a monochromator or the nearly monochromatic yellow emission from a sodium lamp, can be assigned a certain brightness in candles and can also be measured in physical units such as watts. The relationship is contained in the standard visibility curve: At the peak of visibility, 555 nm, one candle corresponds to 0.020 watt, or one watt equals 50 candles. This relation seems discrepant if one thinks, for example, about a 100 watt tungsten lamp, but most of the watts dissipated by a tungsten lamp come in the infrared and are not visible. For monochromatic light at wavelengths other than 555 nm, the candles per watt are less than 50 in proportion to the declining visibility. If the relative visibility (the ordinate on the curve in Fig. 3-3) is called V_{rel} and given the value 1.00 at 555 nm, the candles per watt for monochromatic light are $50V_{rel}$ at any wavelength. Below 400 nm and above 700 nm, V_{rel} is zero and a source of light has no candlepower. For heterochromatic light (mixture of wavelengths) the relation between candles and watts is found by summing the contributions of successive narrow intervals of wavelength as suggested earlier.

A source of one candle is said to give off a *luminous flux* of one candlepower. This flux is the analogue, in these psychological units, of the power in physical units. Luminous flux is also measured in lumens; one candlepower equals 4π lumens. The reason for this new unit has to do with solid angle. In plane geometry the unit of angle is the radian; this is the angle at the center of a circle which subtends an arc equal to the radius. Similarly in three dimensions the unit of solid angle, called the steradian, is that which subtends an area R^2 on a sphere of radius R. It is understood here that the angle is being measured about a point at the center of the sphere. Since the total area of a sphere is $4\pi R^2$, there are 4π steradians around a point (in two dimensions there are 2π radians around a point). Now if one candle gives off a luminous flux of 4π lumens, this amounts to an average of one lumen per steradian. These relations are shown in Fig. 3-4.

If the sphere in Fig. 3-4 has a radius of one foot, the density of flux through it is one lumen per square foot. This measure of *luminous intensity* is called the foot candle. It is the intensity at a distance of one foot from a standard candle. If the radius of the sphere were greater, the flux would be spread over a larger area, so the flux density (intensity) would be less, proportional to the square of the radius. Thus at a distance of one meter the intensity is about one-tenth that at one foot. The intensity one meter from a standard candle is called one lux, or one meter candle; it equals one lumen per square meter. For completeness we should list the phot, which is one lumen per square centimeter. Comparing the squares of these distances, we find that one foot candle equals 10.8 lux and 10,000 lux equal one phot. Since there are 4π lumens in one candle, and 50 candles equal one watt at 555 nm, the lumens per watt at this wavelength are $50 \times 4\pi$, or (more precisely) 621. Finally, taking into account the conversion between square feet and square centimeters, one can derive the conversion between radiant (physical) intensity in watts/cm^2 and luminous intensity in foot candles:

$$1 \text{ watt/cm}^2 = 5.75 \times 10^5 \text{ foot candles at 555 nm}$$

and at any wavelength,

$$1 \text{ watt/cm}^2 = 5.75 \times 10^5 V_{rel} \text{ foot candles} \qquad (3\text{-}2)$$

where V_{rel} is the relative visibility as defined earlier.

Because units such as lux and foot candles are geared to human vision, they are useful in specifying safe or comfortable levels of illumination in schools, factories, and so forth. For the same reason these units are not useful and can be quite misleading when used in other contexts. For example, certain photosynthetic bacteria grow well at the expense of infrared light energy, whereas visible light is

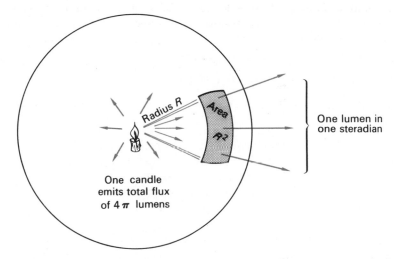

Fig. 3-4. *A source of one candle is said to emit a luminous flux of 4π lumens, or an average of one lumen per steradian. The steradian is a unit of solid angle which subtends an area R^2 on a sphere of radius R. In this drawing it is assumed that the flux is uniform in all directions.*

relatively useless for their growth. Ordinary fluorescent lamps, rich in visible light and hence in candlepower, are deficient in infrared and therefore poor for the growth of these bacteria. A bank of tungsten lamps of much dimmer appearance, but rich in infrared emission, will meanwhile support luxuriant growth.

Usually where light intensity is specified in foot candles, lux, or other such units, the author means that a foot-candle meter (i.e., a kind of photographic exposure meter) gave a certain reading. The relationship between this reading and the physiological effectiveness of the light depends not only on the spectral composition of the light and the relative effectiveness of each wavelength but also on the sensitivity of the meter to light of different wavelengths. In order for this information to be meaningful, the author should at least specify the type of lamp and the manufacturer of the light meter. Even so, this places a great burden of computation or inference on the reader. It would be more informative to specify the radiation field in physical units (energy or quanta) as a function of wavelength, in the manner indicated by Fig. 3-1.

MEASURING THE ABSORPTION OF LIGHT

3-3. *Extinction Coefficient; Optical Density; Percent Transmitted and Absorbed*

Consider a beam of light passing through a solution of light-absorbing material, and for the moment ignore such complications as reflection at the walls of the container, absorption by the solvent, and turbidity or fluorescence of the solution. Imagine a flat layer of solution perpendicular to the beam, and let this layer have a thickness dx, as shown in Fig. 3-5. The intensity of the beam is I as it enters the layer and has a lower value I' as it leaves. Note that if the light-absorbing solute is of concentration C, the quantity $C\,dx$ measures the amount of solute per unit area of the layer:

$$C = \frac{\text{amount of solute}}{\text{volume}} = \frac{\text{amount of solute}}{\text{area} \times \text{thickness}}$$

so

$$C \times \text{thickness} = C\,dx = \frac{\text{amount of solute}}{\text{area}}$$

Now if the amount of light-absorbing material is sufficiently small, the fraction of light absorbed is also very small and is proportional to the amount of material per unit area in the layer:

$$\frac{I - I'}{I} \sim C\,dx$$

if $I - I'$ is a small fraction of I. Call the change of intensity dI; this is a small negative quantity equal to $I' - I$. Let α be the proportionality constant; then

$$\frac{-dI}{I} = \alpha C \, dx \tag{3-3}$$

The constant α is called the absorption coefficient of the material. It is a measure of the strength of absorption, and its value depends both on the type of material and on the wavelength of the light.

For a solution of finite thickness, such that the fraction of light absorbed is no longer very small, Eq. (3-3) can be integrated. However, if the light is heterochromatic (mixture of wavelengths), the integration must be performed separately for each narrow wavelength region, since α varies with wavelength. With this in mind, consider a layer of material of finite thickness x in the direction of the light beam (Fig. 3-6). The light, now considered monochromatic, enters with intensity I_0 and emerges with a lower intensity I_x. The relation between I_0 and I_x is obtained by integrating Eq. (3-3) between the limits zero and x for distance and I_0 and I_x for intensity. The result [compare the derivation of Eq. (2-11) from (2-10)] is

$$I_x = I_0 \, e^{-\alpha C x} \tag{3-4}$$

or

$$\ln \frac{I_0}{I_x} = \alpha C x \tag{3-5}$$

Recognizing that $\ln y$ equals $2.3 \log_{10} y$,

$$\log_{10} \frac{I_0}{I_x} = \frac{\alpha}{2.3} C x \tag{3-6}$$

We now write ϵ for $\alpha/2.3$ and define $\log_{10}(I_0/I_x)$ as the optical density OD of the sample:

$$\mathrm{OD} = \log_{10} \frac{I_0}{I_x} = \epsilon C x \tag{3-7}$$

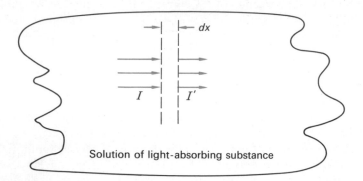

Fig. 3-5. *A beam of light passes through a thickness dx of a solution containing a light-absorbing substance. As it does its intensity decreases from I to I'. Further description and analysis in the text.*

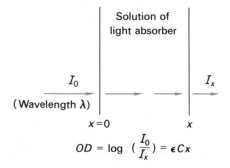

Fig. 3-6. *A beam of monochromatic light passes through a thickness x of a solution containing a light-absorbing substance at a concentration C. The substance has an extinction coefficient ϵ at the particular wavelength used. The intensity of the beam is attenuated from I_0 to I_x according to the formula shown. The logarithm (to base 10) of I_0/I_x is called the optical density OD.*

For solutions the OD is directly proportional to the concentration C of the light absorber and to the length x of the path of the light as it penetrates the sample. The coefficient ϵ is called the extinction coefficient. Like α it is a measure of the intensity of absorption. Its units are reciprocal to those of the product Cx, since OD, being a logarithm, has no dimensions. Thus if C is in molar concentration (M) and x is in centimeters, the units of ϵ are M^{-1} cm^{-1}. It should be emphasized that ϵ is a function of wavelength and Eqs. (3-4) through (3-7) are valid only for monochromatic light. By monochromatic we mean, in this case, light covering such a narrow span of wavelengths that ϵ is effectively constant. Equation (3-4), or any of its variants [Eqs. (3-5) through (3-7)], is known as Beer's law.

It is easy to show that for a solution containing several substances at concentrations $C_1, C_2, \ldots$ and having extinction coefficients $\epsilon_1, \epsilon_2, \ldots$, the OD equals the sum of the separate OD's of the components:

$$\frac{-dI}{I} = (\alpha_1 C_1 + \alpha_2 C_2 + \cdots)\, dx$$

$$\Big\downarrow \text{(Integration)}$$

$$I_x = I_0 \exp\left[-(\alpha_1 C_1 + \alpha_2 C_2 + \cdots)x\right]$$

or

$$\text{OD} = (\epsilon_1 C_1 + \epsilon_2 C_2 + \cdots)x = \text{OD}_1 + \text{OD}_2 + \cdots \qquad (3\text{-}8)$$

Thus the OD has two traits that are extremely useful for analytical purposes: It is proportional to the concentration of a single substance, and it is additive for a mixture of substances.

The absorption of light is used, in experiments, in two distinct ways: as a tool for general chemical analysis and as an agent in photochemical studies. We have seen that in the analytical context the logarithmic measure, OD, is useful. In the other context (photochemical agent) one usually wants to know the rate at which light is being absorbed so as to relate this to the rate of the photochemical reaction. The rate of light absorption in the case of Fig. 3-6 is simply the input minus the output, $I_0 - I_x$. This is usually expressed in terms of A, the fraction absorbed, or T, the fraction transmitted:

$$T = \frac{I_x}{I_0} \tag{3-9}$$

$$A = 1 - T = \frac{I_0 - I_x}{I_0} \tag{3-10}$$

$$\text{Rate of absorption} = AI_0 \tag{3-11}$$

Note that A, T, and OD are related as follows:

$$\text{OD} = \log \frac{1}{T} = -\log T = -\log(1 - A) \tag{3-12}$$

Research in photochemistry and photobiology often involves the measurement of small OD's or small changes in OD. Equation (3-12) can then be modified in two useful ways. First, using the relation

$$\ln(1 + x) \approx x \qquad \text{when } x \ll 1$$

we obtain

$$\log(1 - A) = \frac{1}{2.3} \ln(1 - A) \approx \frac{-A}{2.3}$$

or

$$\text{OD} \approx \frac{A}{2.3} \qquad \text{when } \begin{cases} \text{OD} \ll 1 \\ A \ll 1 \end{cases} \tag{3-13}$$

Second, if a change in OD is much less than 1, we can differentiate Eq. (3-12):

$$d(\text{OD}) = -d\log T = \frac{-dT}{2.3T}$$

or, dropping the notation of differentials and representing a change by Δ,

$$-\Delta(\text{OD}) \approx \frac{\Delta T}{2.3T} \qquad \text{when } \begin{cases} \Delta(\text{OD}) \ll 1 \\ \Delta T \ll T \end{cases} \tag{3-14}$$

Thus with sufficiently weak absorbers or sufficiently small changes, the logarithmic and linear measures of light absorption become almost equivalent.

3-4. *Practical Difficulties in Measuring Light Absorption*

The foregoing development was made without regard for certain practical difficulties which usually attend absorption measurements; namely:

1. The sample is held in a cell whose walls reflect light.
2. The solvent or the cell absorbs light.
3. The sample is fluorescent.
4. The sample scatters light.

The first two of these effects are compensated (the first approximately and the second exactly) by relating the measurement to a reference measurement in which the cell contains only solvent. The OD is still defined as $\log(I_0/I_x)$, but I_0 is not the intensity incident on the sample cell; it is the intensity leaving the reference cell (Fig. 3-7).

If the sample is fluorescent, it will reemit some of the absorbed light, as sketched in Fig. 3-8. For most purposes we want to know the absorption irrespective of whether the light is reemitted as fluorescence. Any fluorescence reaching the detector will therefore spoil the absorption measurement, causing us to overestimate I_x and hence to underestimate the OD. Fortunately the fluorescence is radiated in all directions, whereas the measuring beam can be kept well collimated (compact). Then if the detector is far from the sample and has a window just large enough to admit the measuring beam, very little of the fluorescence will be detected. Also the wavelength(s) of the fluorescence is not, in general, the same as that of the measuring beam. If the detection system is made preferentially responsive to the measuring wavelength, for example, by placing a suitable color filter in front of the detector, then the problem of fluorescence can be avoided.

In practice the problem of fluorescence is usually far less serious, in absorption measurements, than is the problem of scattering. If the sample has even a slight degree of cloudiness or opalescence, an appreciable fraction of the incident light is being scattered in all

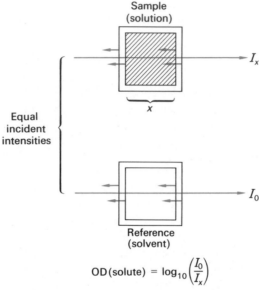

$$OD(\text{solute}) = \log_{10}\left(\frac{I_0}{I_x}\right)$$

Fig. 3-7. In order to compensate for reflections by the cell and absorption by the solvent, a measurement of optical density is related to a reference measurement with solvent in the cell. The OD of the solute is then defined operationally as shown.

directions (again see Fig. 3-8, but imagine that the dashed arrows represent scattering of the incident light rather than fluorescence). The scattered light has the same wavelength as the incident (measuring) light. Scattering can be thought of in either of two ways: as a sort of reflection from the surfaces of many small particles or as an absorption-emission process in which all the absorbed light is re-emitted with no change in its wavelength. The theory is not simple, but some of the practical consequences can be described simply. In the arrangement of Fig. 3-8, scattering detracts from the amount of light reaching the detector. It therefore mimics the effect of absorption and introduces a spurious contribution to the OD. This effect can be alleviated by collecting as much of the scattered light as possible:

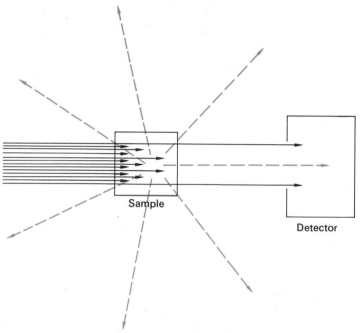

Fig. 3-8. A beam of light is sent through a sample and on to a detector. Part of the light is absorbed by the sample and part is transmitted to the detector. Some of the absorbed light is reemitted in all directions as fluorescence (dashed arrows). The same drawing illustrates the scattering of incident light in all directions in the case of a turbid sample, with scattered light represented by the dashed arrows.

by providing the detector with a large window close to the sample. This is just opposite to the procedure for minimizing the *fluorescence error*. Another way to reduce the error caused by scattering is shown in Fig. 3-9. The error is compensated by introducing large, equal scattering effects in both the sample and the reference measurements.

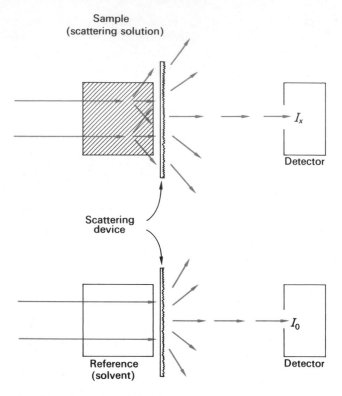

Fig. 3-9.   Compare with Fig. 3-7. The error due to scattering by the sample can be compensated somewhat by adding a strong scatterer to both the sample and the reference measurements. The scattering device can be a piece of ground glass or opal glass or a piece of oil-soaked paper.

The spurious "OD" due to scattering can itself be made useful as a measure of the amount of scattering material, but only after a careful calibration ("OD" versus concentration of material) with the particular apparatus to be used. This technique, called turbidimetry or nephelometry, is used commonly for monitoring the growth of cultures of bacteria.

A more subtle effect of scattering is to intensify the "true" absorption by increasing the effective path of the light through the absorbing material. On the average the light takes a more tortuous path in traversing a turbid sample than in crossing a clear one. This effect can be dramatic, increasing the OD as much as fourfold, and it is not alleviated by the methods described earlier. The best that one can do is to add known amounts of a dye to the scattering sample and see by what factor the absorption by the known dye is intensified due to the scattering.

The analytical use of absorption spectrometry, as exemplified by the equation $OD = \epsilon Cx$, is thus rendered difficult and inexact when the scattering is strong. But in many applications (see later in this chapter) we are interested in the rate of light absorption without reference to the amount of light-absorbing material. We then need to know the fractional absorption A. This can be measured accurately, even in strongly scattering samples, by a technique that measures *all* the light leaving the sample, regardless of its direction. This is equivalent to wrapping the detector around the sample. The technique (see Fig. 3-10) is to surround the sample with a white diffuse reflector known as an integrating sphere. The purpose is to make the light practically uniform throughout the interior of the sphere. The average intensity in the chamber is then measured by sampling the light that emerges through a small port, typically at right angles to the incoming beam. The measurement is made under two conditions:

1. The incoming beam hits the sample. The detector samples a quantity of light $Q(\text{hit})$.
2. The incoming beam just misses the sample. The detector samples a quantity of light $Q(\text{miss})$.

It can be shown (solve Prob. 12 at the end of this chapter) that the ratio of $Q(\text{hit})/Q(\text{miss})$ gives the fraction T of incident light that is *not* absorbed by the sample in the "hit" case. This includes all reflected, scattered, and transmitted components. The fraction that is absorbed by the sample is $A = 1 - T$. Then if light is entering the

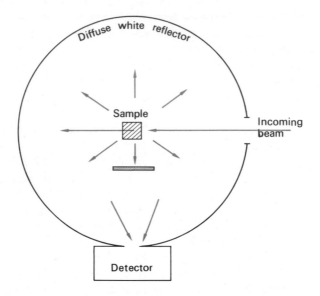

Fig. 3-10.   An integrating sphere; the detector sees an average of the light that is not absorbed by the sample. The mask, which is white, prevents any direct reflection of incoming light to the detector. Further details are in the text and in Prob. 12 at the end of this chapter.

system at a rate I_0, the rate of absorption by the sample in the "hit" case is AI_0, or

$$\text{Rate of absorption} = I_0 \left[1 - \frac{Q(\text{hit})}{Q(\text{miss})} \right] \qquad (3\text{-}15)$$

Some improvement in accuracy is obtained if, in the "miss" case, the beam strikes a nonabsorbing dummy having roughly the same reflecting and scattering characteristics as the sample. This might in some applications be simply a dilute milk suspension. An easy way to make an integrating sphere is to construct a regular dodecahedron out of diffuse white cardboard.

Still another problem that arises especially in the organized structures of living things is the *sieve effect*. It is clear that a bottle of blue ink in the bathtub does not cause a conspicuous blue color as long as the lid is kept on. If the ink is distributed throughout the bath water, the blueness is much increased. Similarly the amount of pigment in a system (for example, in a living cell) might be underestimated if it is concentrated in packets. The error will be serious if a single packet absorbs an appreciable fraction of the light falling on it. A quantitative approach to the sieve effect is illustrated in Prob. 11.

ABSORPTION AND EMISSION; ANALYTICAL USES

3-5. *Analysis by Absorption Spectrometry*

Now that ϵ and OD have been defined as measures of the intensity of absorption, the absorption spectra sketched in Figs. 2-16 and 2-18 can be put on a quantitative basis: They can be regarded as plots of ϵ or OD versus frequency or wavelength.

The absorption spectra of actual molecules often show several bands, or regions, of strong absorption, each of a characteristic height ϵ_m and wavelength λ_m at the maximum. These spectra are therefore important tools for the identification and quantitative estimation of substances. Furthermore a chemical reaction can often be monitored quickly and accurately by the change in absorption spectrum, from that of the reactants to that of the products. A striking example is found in the reactions of cytochromes, an important class of biological electron transport catalysts. These iron-containing proteins undergo reversible oxidation and reduction with gain or loss of one electron per iron atom:

$$Cyt(Fe^{3+}) + e^- \rightleftarrows Cyt(Fe^{++})$$

The highly characteristic spectra of oxidized (Fe^{3+}) and reduced (Fe^{++}) cytochrome *c* from horse heart muscle are shown in Fig. 3-11, together with the "difference spectrum, reduced minus oxidized" that describes the change of absorption spectrum in going from the

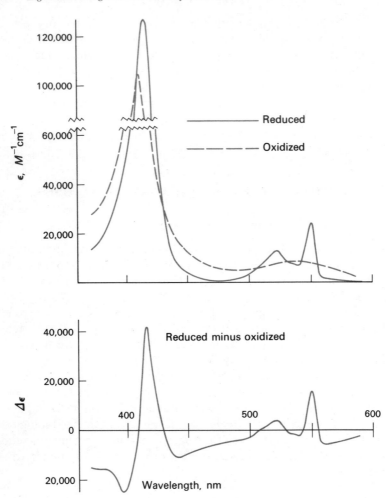

Fig. 3-11. Absorption spectra (extinction coefficient versus wavelength) of cytochrome c from horse heart in its reduced and oxidized forms and the difference, reduced minus oxidized. Adapted from data by E. Margoliash, p. 273 in The Encyclopedia of Biochemistry by R. J. Williams and E. M. Lansford, Jr., Eds. © 1967, by Reinhold Publishing Corp., by permission of Van Nostrand Reinhold Co.

oxidized to the reduced form. The value of ϵ at 550 nm is 25×10^3 M^{-1} cm^{-1} for reduced cytochrome c and 8×10^3 M^{-1} cm^{-1} for the oxidized form. The difference, 17×10^3 M^{-1} cm^{-1}, is the *differential extinction coefficient* $\Delta\epsilon$ for the change from oxidized to reduced. Then if the progress of the reduction is being monitored by the change in optical density at 550 nm, the amount of cytochrome that has been converted is given by

$$\Delta(\text{OD}) = (\Delta\epsilon)(\Delta C)x$$

or

$$\Delta C = \frac{\Delta\text{OD}}{x\,\Delta\epsilon} \tag{3-16}$$

for the change in molar concentration of either form.

Since the common commercially available absorption spectrometers (called spectrophotometers) have limiting sensitivities of the order of OD $= 10^{-3}$, and since the more intense absorption bands of organic molecules have peak ϵ's of 10^4 to 10^5 M^{-1} cm^{-1}, the sensitivity of this method extends to about 10^{-8} M with a sample in a 1-cm cell. With special care the sensitivity can be extended about two orders of magnitude further, to about 10^{-10} M.

3-6. Analysis by Fluorescence and Phosphorescence

The fluorescence of a molecule sometimes affords a far more sensitive test of its presence than the absorption. This is especially true if the quantum efficiency, or yield, of the fluorescence (quanta emitted/quanta absorbed) is high and the excitation can be performed at a wavelength far removed from the wavelength of measurement. As an example of the latter condition see Fig. 2-32, where light absorbed in the higher transition (shorter-wave absorption band) will lead to emission from the lower one. Under these favorable conditions it is not difficult to measure a level of fluorescence less than 10^{-7} times that of the beam that excites the fluorescence. If the fluorescence yield is high, so that an appreciable fraction of the absorbed light is reemitted, this corresponds to a fractional absorption less than 10^{-7} or an OD of the order of 10^{-8}. Such sensitivity is about 1,000 times greater than the limiting sensitivity of absorption measurements.

Unfortunately many organic molecules are only weakly fluorescent; and even if the fluorescence is strong, the spectrum of fluorescence is less distinctive than the absorption spectrum, because only the lowest transition (longest-wave absorption band) is accompanied by appreciable fluorescence (again see Fig. 2-32). But even though the spectrum is less informative than an absorption spectrum, the intensity of the fluorescence is often far more informative than any aspect of an absorption measurement. This is because the intensity of fluorescence gives information about competing mechanisms for going from the excited state to the ground state, and these mechanisms are usually of first importance in photobiology. As an example consider the use of a fluorescent dye as a probe for changes in the structure of a protein. Here the technique is to attach a dye molecule to the protein molecule with the expectation that a slight change in the electrochemical environment of the dye will alter its fluorescence yield.[1] Then a subtle change in the configuration of the protein can be detected with great sensitivity through its effect on the fluorescence of the dye.

Most commonly the "ordinary" or prompt fluorescence is far more intense than any delayed fluorescence or phosphorescence. The latter two can be especially interesting, however, because they signify the involvement of metastable conditions, as indicated in Fig. 2-22. These different kinds of emission can be distinguished by their lifetimes and by their spectra in relation to the absorption spectrum.

The longer-lived emissions can be singled out, even in the presence of a great preponderance of prompt fluorescence, by means of a phosphoroscope. This is a device for introducing a time delay between photoexcitation of the sample and measurement of the consequent emission. Several forms of phosphoroscope, practical in different situations, are shown in Fig. 3-12.

---

[1] Some molecules become much more strongly fluorescent when they are constrained so that relative movements of different parts of the molecule are hindered. The restriction appears to eliminate pathways for radiationless deexcitation and thus allow more fluorescence.

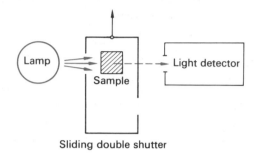

Sliding double shutter

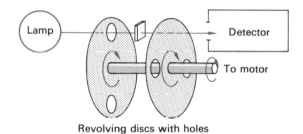

Revolving discs with holes

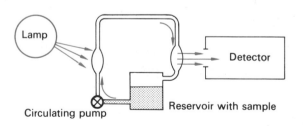

Fig. 3-12. Three ways to measure delayed fluorescence or phosphorescence by imposing a time separation between excitation and measurement of the emission.

With mechanical shutters, rotating discs, or pumps it is difficult to reduce the delay between excitation and measurement below about 10^{-4} sec. Such an interval is long enough that a prompt fluorescence of mean lifetime 10^{-8} sec will have decayed to a negligibly small level during the time between excitation and measurement. For the shorter times needed to measure prompt fluorescence, one must use flash lamps and electronic shutters or switching devices or else eliminate

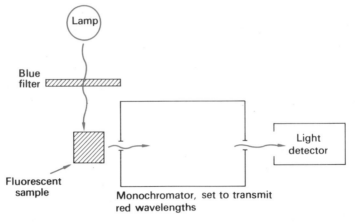

Fig. 3-13. *A typical arrangement for measuring fluorescence spectra while preventing scattered exciting light from reaching the detector. In this example the exciting light is blue, and the fluorescence in the red part of the spectrum is measured.*

the time delay altogether. In the latter procedure the detector is exposed to emission from the sample at the same time that the sample is being excited. This raises a new problem: Light from the exciting lamp, scattered by the sample into the detector, is registered falsely as emission. This false signal is eliminated by judicious use of color filters and/or monochromators such that all wavelengths of exciting light that reach the sample are prevented from reaching the detector. An arrangement of this kind, designed for the measurement of emission spectra, is shown in Fig. 3-13. The particular choice of exciting and measuring wavelengths would of course vary with the substance being measured.

3-7. *Relations among Absorption Intensity, Fluorescence Lifetime, and Fluorescence Yield*

It was mentioned earlier that the probability of a downward transition, accompanied by fluorescence, is proportional to that of the corresponding upward transition (absorption). The first of these two probabilities governs the intrinsic lifetime in the excited state—that is, the lifetime that would prevail if fluorescence provided the only mechanism for deexcitation. The intrinsic lifetime [τ_0; see Eq. (2-14)] is therefore inversely proportional to the probability for absorption, which in turn can be measured by the area under the absorption band. For a useful formulation of this relation refer to Fig. 3-14. Following tradition, we define the wave number k as the reciprocal of the wavelength λ. Its conventional units are cm^{-1}, corresponding to λ measured in centimeters rather than nanometers. The figure shows an absorption band for the transition in question, plotted as the molar extinction coefficient ϵ (M^{-1} cm^{-1}) versus k (cm^{-1}). The area under this band is roughly equal to the peak height ϵ_m times the width at half-maximum Δk. Taking this formulation of area, the relation is

$$\frac{1}{\tau_0} = 3 \times 10^{-9} k_m{}^2 \, \Delta k \, \epsilon_m \qquad (3\text{-}17)$$

In this formula the quantity k_m is the wave number at the absorption peak. The factor $3 \times 10^{-9} k_m{}^2$ takes account of the proportionality between the probabilities for emission and absorption. This equation is accurate within about ± 30 percent for the radiative transitions that correspond to intense absorption bands of pigments. The accuracy can be brought to within 5 percent by the use of a more sophisticated treatment involving integration over both the absorption band and the fluorescence band.

It must be remembered, of course, that Eq. (3-17) gives the intrinsic lifetime; the actual lifetime is shorter, because deexcitation can occur by a variety of nonfluorescent mechanisms. The ratio of actual to intrinsic lifetime gives the quantum yield of the fluorescence, as shown by Eq. (2-15). Thus if one fluorescent quantum emerges for

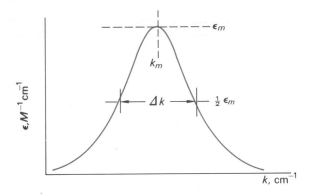

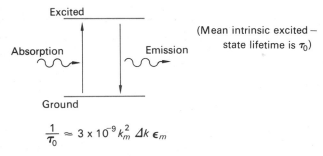

$$\frac{1}{\tau_0} \approx 3 \times 10^{-9} k_m^2 \, \Delta k \, \epsilon_m$$

Fig. 3-14.   An absorption spectrum can be plotted as extinction coefficient versus wave number (reciprocal of wavelength). Excited-state lifetime is the related to the area under the corresponding absorption band, as shown here. See the text for a more complete discussion. Also see Prob. 13.

every ten quanta absorbed, the fluorescence quantum yield ϕ_f is 10 percent and the actual lifetime is predicted to be one-tenth the intrinsic value as computed from Eq. (3-17). Information about excited-state lifetime can thus be obtained by combining two relatively easy measurements: the area under the absorption band and the quantum yield of fluorescence. If the lifetime can also be measured directly from the decay of fluorescence, the result can provide a useful check against the value predicted by the indirect method. Any discrepancy will suggest that something is not straightforward. These considerations have played a large part in showing that green plants contain more than one type of chlorophyll with different fluorescence properties and different photochemical functions.

QUANTUM EFFICIENCY

3-8. The Significance of Quantum Efficiency Measurements in Photochemistry

The meaning of quantum efficiency is rooted in the idea, first expressed by Einstein, that a single quantum absorbed by a molecule can bring about the photochemical alteration of that molecule. In consequence one can expect a simple numerical relationship, or stoichiometry, between quanta absorbed and molecules of photochemical products. This relationship can be expressed as the quantum yield, or efficiency, (molecules or equivalents of photoproduct per quantum absorbed) or as its reciprocal, the quantum requirement. The measurement of quantum efficiency, by revealing the stoichiometry, can often give basic information about photochemical mechanisms.

Even a crude measure of quantum efficiency can sometimes be very revealing. In photobiology we are often confronted with light effects that are striking and potentially interesting but that may or may not be major effects in terms of the system we are studying. For example, light striking the eye causes certain very rapid voltages to appear: Are these a part of the mechanism of seeing, or are they side-effects of no direct importance? Again, in photosynthesis light causes the reversible oxidation and reduction of a very few (perhaps one out of 300) chlorophyll molecules. Is this part of the primary photochemical act of photosynthesis, or is it a nonessential and perhaps deleterious reaction? Considerable insight can be gained in these questions if it can be shown merely that the quantum efficiency is very low or respectably high. The importance of a phenomenon is established if it can be shown that most of the quanta absorbed by the system bring about that phenomenon.

There are many ways in which a simple stoichiometry between light quanta and molecules of photoproduct can be submerged by complications, making a useful evaluation of the quantum efficiency more difficult. Some of these complications are fundamental, involving basic physical mechanisms, and some are merely technical.

If the photochemical alteration of a molecule can be caused by promoting the molecule to the lowest excited electronic state, then one quantum of sufficient energy can bring this about. If a quantum of higher energy is absorbed, so that a higher excited state is attained, the excess energy is nearly always dissipated through a very rapid radiationless decay to the lowest excited state, as indicated in Sec. 2-14. The higher-energy quantum then has no more value for photochemistry than the lesser one. On the other hand it is possible that 2 quanta, each one insufficient to cause excitation, can pool their energies and raise a molecule to an excited state. The circumstances allowing this are rare, however, and there is no evidence at present that such biphotonic or 2-quantum cooperative mechanisms are significant in photobiology. Finally it is possible that one quantum can set off a chain reaction much as a spark ignites a pool of gasoline. An example is the photochemical ignition of a reaction between hydrogen and chlorine:

$$Light:\quad Cl_2 \xrightarrow{h\nu} 2Cl$$

followed by

$$Dark:\quad \begin{cases} Cl + H_2 \rightarrow HCl + H \\ H + Cl_2 \rightarrow HCl + Cl, \text{ etc.} \end{cases}$$

Again we know of no case of this special kind that is significant in photobiology. Barring unexpected developments, we can proceed profitably by expecting a simple stoichiometric relation between light quanta and photochemical products.

Aside from these more fundamental matters, there are various technical reasons that the input-output relation between light quanta and photochemical product can become complicated. First of all, a quantum must be absorbed in order to cause excitation and thereby have a photochemical effect (Grotthus-Draper law). If the photo-chemically active pigment is screened by an inert pigment, those quanta absorbed by the inert pigment are without effect and the measured efficiency is lowered. As a variation, the inert pigment might have some capacity for passing its excitation energy along (transferring a quantum) to the active pigment. In that case the quantum efficiency will be modified according to the probability for such energy transfer. Finally there is the fact, already discussed, that not all cases of excitation lead to photochemistry. One can have fluorescent or radiationless deexcitation as well as photochemical utilization of the quantum, with various probabilities that can be expressed by rate constants (see Sec. 2-15). For these principal reasons, and other less obvious ones, the quantum efficiency for a photochemical process may fall well below the value dictated by the stoichiometry.

3-9. Competition between Fluorescence and Photochemistry

As we saw in Sec. 2-15, the quantum efficiencies of fluorescence and photochemistry are interrelated because these processes are in competition with each other. In fact, if we list all competitive processes by which excited molecules dispose of their energy, the sum of the quantum efficiencies of these processes must be 100 percent. Any increase in the efficiency of one of the processes must be offset by decreases in the others. Using the rate constants described in Sec. 2-15, we find that the quantum efficiencies for fluorescence, radiation-less deexcitation, and photochemical quenching are

$$\text{Fluorescence:} \qquad \phi_f = \frac{k_f}{k_f + k_d + k_p}$$

$$\text{Radiationless deexcitation:} \quad \phi_d = \frac{k_d}{k_f + k_d + k_p} \qquad (3\text{-}18)$$

$$\text{Photochemical quenching:} \quad \phi_p = \frac{k_p}{k_f + k_d + k_p}$$

from which

$$\phi_f + \phi_d + \phi_p = 1.00 \qquad (3\text{-}19)$$

Suppose now that by some trick (such as the application of a poison) we eliminate the photochemical pathway, effectively reducing the value of k_p to zero. Then the photochemical efficiency ϕ_p is zero and the efficiencies of the other processes rise to the higher values

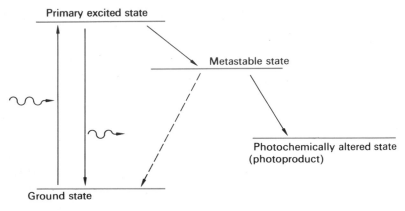

Fig. 3-15.   A photochemical process might be mediated through a metastable state, as shown here. If the photochemical act is blocked, the system might return from the metastable state to the ground state, as shown by the dashed arrow. Any relationship between the efficiencies of fluorescence and photochemistry can then become complicated.

$k_f/(k_f + k_d)$ and $k_d/(k_f + k_d)$ respectively. A great body of research in photosynthesis is based on the simple fact that the fluorescence of the photochemically active pigment (chlorophyll) increases when the photochemistry is poisoned or otherwise blocked. Changes in the fluorescence are symptomatic of changes in the photochemistry, whether the latter can be measured directly or not.

It does not follow, however, that a change in the photochemical efficiency must be attended by a change in the yield of fluorescence. Suppose that the photochemistry proceeds in two steps, with a metastable excited state as an intermediate, as shown in Fig. 3-15.

Now suppose that the second step, conversion from the metastable state to the photochemically altered state, is blocked. To a first approximation this will increase the pool of molecules that are in the metastable state, but will not alter the rate at which the primary excited molecules are being converted to metastable ones. The process that competes with fluorescence, and that is characterized by the rate constant k_p, is the primary conversion from excited state to metastable state. If this process does not change, then the yield of fluorescence does not change either, even if the yield of photoproduct made *from* the metastable state changes radically. Similar remarks can be made for any case where the first observable consequence of the photochemistry is one or more steps removed from the primary photochemical act. In all such cases one must be careful about the definition of photochemistry and photochemical efficiency. In the case just described, the quantum efficiency for the pathway through the metastable state is one thing, and the efficiency for the formation of a particular photoproduct is another.

3-10. Excitation Lifetime, Collision Frequency, and Photochemical Efficiency

In many photochemical systems, the involvement of a metastable state as an intermediate has actually been shown most convincingly through measurement of the quantum efficiency. This has been true in cases where the chemistry depends on random collisions between molecules in solution. Consider the case of Fig. 2-27*b*, in which the sensitizer S (pigment) in its excited state reacts with an electron donor D to form D+ and S−. If this process is collision-dependent, then a molecule of D must collide with one of S while the latter is in an excited state. Now suppose that the reaction is observed to proceed with moderately high quantum efficiency, say 10 percent, under the following conditions: the concentrations of S and D and the temperature are such that a given molecule of S encounters a molecule of D once every 10^{-3} sec, on the average. This can only mean that the excited state of S, that leads to a photochemical reaction in a collision with D, endures for about 10^{-4} sec or more. If the lifetime were as low as 10^{-8} sec, the chance of a collision with D during this lifetime would be negligibly small. Thus the primary excitation in S, of lifetime about 10^{-8} sec, must be translated into a longer-lived (metastable) state that mediates the photochemistry. Many photochemical systems involving organic molecules in solution have been studied in terms of quantum efficiency versus collision frequency of the reaction partners, and the involvement of a metastable state, of lifetime in the range 0.1 to 10^{-4} sec, has often been implicated. This is probably a triplet state in most cases.

3-11. *Measurement of Fluorescence Efficiency*

To determine the quantum efficiency of a process, we obviously must measure[1] two things: the number of quanta absorbed by the system and the number of units of product. The latter might be quanta in the case of fluorescence, molecules in the case of a chemical product, or even electric dipoles in the case of a bioelectric phenomenon such as vision. The entire problem might also be considered in reverse, as in bioluminescence, where we wish to know how many quanta come out of the system per molecule of chemical input. In most situations the measurements are dynamic; we deal with rates of quantum absorption and product formation.

The rate at which light impinges on a sample is given by the intensity of the incident beam I_0 times the area S intercepted by the sample, as suggested in Fig. 3-2. This incoming flux must be multiplied by the fractional absorption A to give the rate $A I_0 S$ at which the sample absorbs light [recall Eqs. (3-10), (3-11), and (3-15)]. The light should be measured in quanta, corresponding to molecules of a product, or in einsteins, corresponding to moles. One must, of course, take proper account of problems such as reflection losses at the walls of the sample cell.

If the object of study is fluorescence, it is necessary to measure the rate of quantum emission as well as the rate of absorption. In measuring the emission, one must take care to exclude scattered incoming light; this is usually done by means of complementary color filters, as shown in Fig. 3-13. The arrangement must be capable

---

[1] Some practical aspects of these measurements are discussed in the appendixes at the end of this book.

of detecting the entire span of wavelengths that are present in the fluorescence. In any such arrangement the efficiency of detection will vary with the wavelength, because in general the efficiencies of both the monochromator (or filter) and the detector change with wavelength. Next there is a geometrical problem: The fluorescence is emitted in all directions, but the apparatus records only the fraction that passes into the detecting system.

In spite of these problems, which seem formidable at first sight, it is not too difficult to measure absolute quantum efficiencies of fluorescence with fair accuracy (about ±20 per cent) by comparing the "unknown" sample with "standard" substances of known fluorescence properties. First of all the spectral sensitivity, or variation with wavelength, of the detection system can be calibrated by measuring the response to a substance whose emission spectrum is known. This can be either a fluorescent dye of known spectrum or a self-luminous object; in the latter category the simplest device is a tungsten lamp filament operated at a specified temperature (see Appendix A). Next a standard substance of known fluorescence efficiency is chosen; its fluorescence band should be in the same wavelength region as that of the sample being investigated. The concentration of the standard can be adjusted so that it matches the sample in terms of the rate at which incoming light is absorbed. Then the outputs (fluorescences) of the sample and the standard, when adjusted for the previously calibrated wavelength dependence, are in the same ratio as their quantum efficiencies. The output is measured as the area under the emission band (refer to Fig. 3-1). One precaution is important: Both the sample and the standard must be dilute enough that they do not reabsorb a significant fraction of the fluorescence; or if they do, the error introduced by this reabsorption must be computed.

A convenient fluorescence standard is rhodamine B, a dye which emits in the visible region with a well-characterized spectrum and with a quantum efficiency of 95 percent. Another very convenient standard emission spectrum is that of a tungsten lamp, as described in Appendix A. The latter is extremely useful for calibrating the detection system in order to rectify the shapes of emission spectra, whether the quantum efficiency is of interest or not.

3-12. Measurement of Photochemical Efficiency; Two Examples

We turn now to methods for measuring photochemical quantum efficiency, which will be described through two specific examples. First consider the photosynthetic evolution of oxygen by a suspension of green algae, measured in the manner developed by Otto Warburg. The algae are held in a closed vessel connected to a manometer, as shown in Fig. 3-16. Production of oxygen is registered as an increase in pressure; the volume of the system is kept constant by adjusting the manometer fluid reservoir. The manometer fluid is usually chosen to be water with a little detergent and a dye for visibility. The instru-

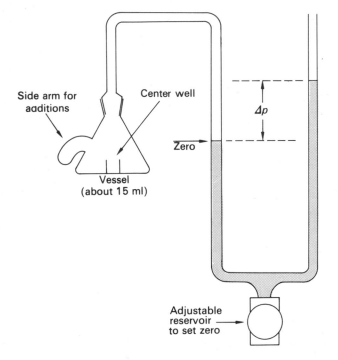

Fig. 3-16. *A Warburg manometer for studying gas exchange reactions in a closed vessel at constant volume. For photochemical studies the vessel can be illuminated from below.*

ment can be calibrated by producing or absorbing a known amount of oxygen or nitrogen through a chemical reaction.

This device, the Warburg manometer, is sensitive to about 1 mm^3 or 5×10^{-8} mole of a gas such as oxygen. It has been used very extensively in biological laboratories for all assays that could be made to involve a gas exchange. Manometry was largely displaced, in the 1950s, by the more convenient spectrophotometric methods (refer to Fig. 3-11).

In Warburg manometry the vessel is held in a constant temperature bath and shaken to ensure equilibration of substances between the liquid and gas phases. For this reason the sample (a suspension of algae in the present illustration) is optically very uneven, and an accurate measurement of light absorption is made possible only by using a dense suspension so that *all* the incident light is absorbed. The rate of light absorption is then simply the incident intensity times the area of the bottom of the vessel occupied by the reacting material, assuming that the light comes from below.

Photosynthesis involves the uptake of carbon dioxide as well as the evolution of oxygen, but any turnover of CO_2 can be nullified by placing a bicarbonate buffer in a center well in the vessel. A more difficult problem arises because the photosynthetic evolution of oxygen is partly offset by an oxygen consumption due to respiration. As a first approximation to solving this problem, one can assume that the respiration in the light proceeds at the same rate as that which can be measured in darkness.

This manometric procedure is illustrated by a numerical example in Prob. 16.

Now let us consider a method based on spectrophotometry, more representative of contemporary situations in photochemical research. In this example a solution of cytochrome, whose optical absorption properties are shown in Fig. 3-11, is mixed with a suspension of broken cells of photosynthetic bacteria. These bacteria contain a pigment, similar to the chlorophyll of green plants, called bacteriochlorophyll. In our example the bacteriochlorophyll has an absorption maximum at 880 nm. The pigmented tissue from the broken cells can bring about the following photochemistry: When light is absorbed by the bacteriochlorophyll, electrons are transferred from the added cytochrome (which thereby becomes oxidized) to an unidentified electron acceptor in the tissue. In the dark the reaction is reversed, the electrons finding their way from the acceptor back to the cytochrome.

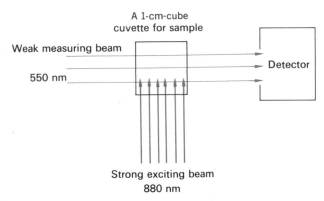

Fig. 3-17.   An arrangement for measuring the quantum efficiency of the photochemical oxidation of cytochrome sensitized by the bacteriochlorophyll in a suspension of broken cells of photosynthetic bacteria. The exciting wavelength is chosen to be absorbed by the bacteriochlorophyll; the measuring wavelength is one at which the oxidation of cytochrome is attended by a suitable change in optical density (see Fig. 3-11). These wavelengths are conveniently isolated by means of optical interference filters.

The mixture is held in a rectangular cuvette illuminated from one side by a weak measuring beam of wavelength 550 nm to monitor the oxidation state of the cytochrome. A stronger beam of wavelength 880 nm, designed to excite the bacteriochlorophyll and thus to drive the photochemistry, is at right angles to the measuring beam. The measuring beam is too weak to cause significant excitation of the bacteriochlorophyll. The arrangement is shown in Fig. 3-17; for simplicity the cuvette is taken to be a 1-cm cube (this restriction is removed in Prob. 18). Then if the incident intensity of the 880-nm exciting light is I_0 einsteins/cm^2 sec and the fraction absorbed by the sample is A, the rate of quantum absorption in the 1-cm cube is $I_0 A$

einsteins/sec. This light is turned on suddenly, after a period of dark adaptation, while the optical density at 550 nm is being monitored and recorded. A typical trace of OD_{550} versus time will look as sketched in Fig. 3-18. The initial "light on" slope of this trace shows

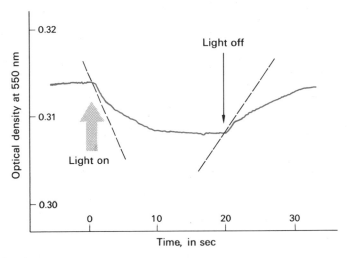

Fig. 3-18.   *A typical record obtained in the experiment illustrated in Fig. 3-17. Quantum efficiencies can be evaluated from the initial "light on" and "light off" slopes of the trace, as explained in the text. The sensitivity and freedom from noise (random fluctuations) shown here can only be obtained with a fine differential spectrophotometer, not with the usual commercial absorption spectrometer.*

the rate at which cytochrome is being oxidized. The amount of cytochrome oxidized is related to the change in optical density through Eq. (3-16),

$$\Delta C = \frac{\Delta OD}{x \, \Delta \epsilon}$$

With x equal to 1 cm and $\Delta \epsilon$ in units of M^{-1} cm^{-1}, the initial rate of cytochrome oxidation is given by

$$\Delta C \, (\text{molar/sec}) = \frac{\Delta OD/\text{sec}}{\Delta \epsilon} \tag{3-20}$$

A change of 1 M concentration corresponds to 10^{-3} moles in a 1-cm cube (equating 1 cm^3 to 10^{-3} liters), so in the cube,

$$\Delta c \text{ (moles/sec)} = \frac{\Delta OD/sec}{10^3 \Delta \epsilon} \qquad (3\text{-}21)$$

In this example the optical density decreases because oxidation of the cytochrome causes a bleaching of the 550-nm band. The question of minus signs can be handled arbitrarily by letting both ΔOD and $\Delta \epsilon$ be negative quantities at 550 nm for the oxidation of the cytochrome, so that Δc (moles of cytochrome oxidized) comes out positive.

The quantum efficiency for cytochrome oxidation equals the number of moles of cytochrome oxidized divided by the einsteins of light absorbed:

$$\phi_p = \frac{\Delta c \text{ (moles/sec)}}{I_0 A \text{ (einsteins/sec)}} = \frac{\Delta OD/sec}{10^3 I_0 A \Delta \epsilon} \qquad (3\text{-}22)$$

When applied to the "light on" slope, this expression gives the photochemical efficiency at the start of illumination after a period of adaptation to darkness. As the reaction proceeds, and products accumulate, the reverse (dark) reaction becomes significant. Eventually a steady state is reached, during continuous illumination, in which the forward light-driven reaction is just balanced by the reverse reaction. The amount of oxidized cytochrome has then reached a constant value, even though there is a continued turnover of cytochrome between its oxidized and reduced forms. Now if the light is turned off abruptly, the forward reaction stops and the rate of the compensating back reaction is revealed by the initial "light off" slope. The "light off" slope can therefore be used as an indirect measure of the light-driven reaction in the illuminated steady state. The efficiency of this ongoing reaction, which the system can maintain in a steady state, may be of more practical interest than that of the initial "light on" reaction. An accurate measure of the initial slope is deceptively hard to obtain when the curvature (gradual decrease in slope) is present near the start. The usual error is to underestimate the slope by 10 or 20 percent.[1] Of course, the measuring and recording system must be able to respond quickly enough to register the sudden changes in slope faithfully, or the efficiency will be underestimated.

In this experimental construction there is an error, caused by attenuation of the exciting light as it passes through the sample, that must be taken into account or made small. Because the exciting light is absorbed, becoming weaker as it penetrates the sample, the rate of quantum absorption diminishes from one side of the measuring beam to the other. The rate of photochemistry diminishes concomitantly. If the system were able to record the average rate of photochemistry (going across the measuring beam), this could be divided by the average rate of quantum absorption for a proper measure of quantum efficiency. However, the measuring beam detector sees only the total light coming through the cuvette; it takes an average of the transmitted light across the measuring beam. A change in this quantity is not related in any simple way to the average rate of photochemistry, because of the logarithmic relation between transmission and optical density. The measured quantum efficiency will therefore be in error if the sample is too concentrated. This error will be slight (less than about 5 percent) if the fraction of exciting light absorbed by the sample is less than about 50 percent. A numerical example of this kind of measurement is given in Prob. 17.

3-13. Action Spectra; Their Uses and Their Measurement

A powerful technique in photobiology is to analyze the response of the system as a function of the wavelength of the light. In simple photochemical systems this is usually a trivial exercise: The variation with wavelength should, and generally does, reflect the absorption spectrum of the sensitizing pigment. The same should be true in photobiology, but because the system is usually more complicated there is more to be learned. There may be several pigments, some effective and others ineffective for the phenomenon under study. The

---

[1] There is a trick, using a mirror to reflect the initial part of the "light on" or "light off" trace, by which this systematic error can be minimized. Its discovery is left as an exercise for the student.

effective pigment(s) might be present in such small amounts as to be invisible. In these cases an action spectrum, or plot of "effectiveness" of the light versus its wavelength, may reveal what pigment is involved or may even show the existence of a hitherto undiscovered pigment.

The first problem in determining an action spectrum is to define and quantify the response. Often this is easy, as with the rate of oxygen evolution by an illuminated leaf, or the angle through which a sunflower has bent in facing toward a light source, or the fraction killed in a population of bacteria given a dose of ultraviolet. In some cases the response is harder to quantify, but a single *standard response* can be described, as with the first perceptible reddening of a patch of skin in an experiment on sunburn.

A simple procedure would be to measure the response in question at a succession of wavelengths, taking care to preserve equal light intensities (quanta/cm^2 sec) at all wavelengths, and then to plot the size of the response versus wavelength. This method cannot be used unless a succession of graded responses can be defined. Even if the response is readily made quantitative, as with a photochemical rate, its magnitude might not be simply proportional to light intensity. A more complicated relation between response and light intensity will then be translated into a distortion of the shape of the action spectrum: Peaks will be "unnaturally" flattened or exaggerated relative to the absorption spectrum.

These difficulties are avoided by following a slightly different procedure. A single standard magnitude is chosen for the response, and at each wavelength the light intensity is found that will produce that response.[1] Less light will of course be needed at the wavelengths of greater effectiveness. The reciprocal of the intensity needed for a standard response is thus a measure of the effectiveness of the light; this is plotted against wavelength to produce an action spectrum. The rationality of this procedure will now be defended for a case where the response is well defined: for the photochemical oxidation of cytochrome discussed in the last section.

---

[1] This procedure can sometimes be facilitated by interpolation between measured responses that are slightly larger and smaller than the standard one.

Equation (3-22) can be rewritten in the form

$$\frac{1}{I_0} = \frac{1}{R} A \phi_p \qquad (3\text{-}23)$$

where the quantity R (response) is substituted for $(\Delta OD/sec)/10^3 \Delta \epsilon$ or moles/cm^3 sec of photoproduct. We have thus defined the response as the rate at which a product is made. Now suppose that

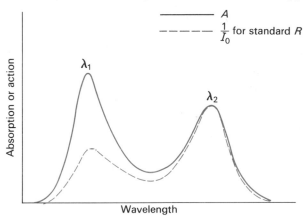

Fig. 3-19. Hypothetical absorption and action spectra normalized to agree at the second absorption peak λ_2. For discussion see the text.

we choose a particular value of R as a standard response and determine at each wavelength the value of I_0 that is needed to give this response. Having stipulated that R is constant, let us suppose for the moment that ϕ_p is also constant (independent of wavelength). Then by Eq. (3-23), a plot of $1/I_0$ versus wavelength (the action spectrum) should have the same shape as a plot of A versus wavelength (the absorption spectrum). A comparison of these plots is thus a test of whether or not the quantum efficiency ϕ_p actually is constant, or whether it varies with wavelength. This test can be informative even when R and I_0 are not defined or known in absolute terms, as indicated in Fig. 3-19. Here the two plots have been adjusted so as to have the same height at λ_2, and the plot of $1/I_0$ is deficient at λ_1. This shows that the value of ϕ_p for the band at λ_1 is about half the value at λ_2.

In Eq. (3-23) the parameters are expressed or conceived as rates: einsteins/sec for light and moles/sec for the response. An equivalent equation could be written in which the parameters are cumulative: in which the light intensity I_0 is replaced by a total dose of light Q_0 and the response R is thought of as a total quantity of product. This would correspond to an integration of Eq. (3-23) over some period of time. The integrated or cumulative form would lend itself naturally to situations in which the total dose of light appears to be decisive for the phenomenon, or in which the response should be visualized as a certain quantity rather than a rate. Thus the formulation can be adapted, within limits, to the requirements of the situation. The use of action spectra can be extended to any light-dependent phenomenon for which a standard response can be defined; for example, one might determine an action spectrum for the light-induced germination of lettuce seeds, using for "standard R" the criterion that 50 percent of the seeds germinate within two weeks, or an action spectrum for sunburn, using an arbitrary degree of reddening as the end point. An operationally useful standard response is usually about one-half the maximum possible response.

Note that the action spectrum, $1/I_0$ (standard R) versus wavelength, should be compared with an absorption spectrum showing A versus λ and not OD versus λ. These two versions of the absorption spectrum are similar in shape only if OD and A are small [see Eq. (3-13)]. If the experimental preparation is too concentrated, the fraction of light absorbed is close to 100 percent at all wavelengths, and all features corresponding to peaks and troughs in the absorption spectrum are washed out. These features will be washed out in the action spectrum as well, but the action spectrum will then show most clearly all variations of the quantum efficiency with wavelength. The spectrum will simply not show how these variations are related to the characteristic absorption bands of particular pigments. Thus the choice of concentration depends partly on what features are to be developed in the action spectrum. These considerations are explored in Prob. 19.

Unfortunately the action spectrum can be distorted in unnatural ways if the preparation is too concentrated. Referring to the experimental construction of Fig. 3-17, imagine that the absorption at 880 nm (absorption peak of bacteriochlorophyll) is so strong that almost all the exciting light is absorbed within a shallow layer of the sample at the surface of incidence. In that case very little light is available in the part of the sample that is traversed by the 550-nm measuring beam. Even with strong excitation, the observable reaction sets in very slowly. Now imagine that the exciting wavelength is changed to 700 nm, where the absorption by the sample happens to be much less. At this wavelength a significant intensity of light can penetrate to the region in the sample that is monitored by the measuring beam. Even though the fractional absorption is less at 700 nm, the greater light intensity in the "measuring zone" more than compensates and the effectiveness of the light is greater than it is at 880 nm. In this way an action spectrum can show the curious distortion of displaying peaks where the troughs should be, and vice versa. To avoid this kind of trouble, it is necessary to use a dilute preparation, or preferably to measure the action spectrum with a series of samples of different concentrations.

Historically the measurement of action spectra has provided much valuable information and also much avoidable confusion. When measured carefully and properly, the action spectrum is of greatest value in photobiology.

BIBLIOGRAPHY

1. Sears, F. W.: "Optics," 3d ed., Addison-Wesley Publishing Company, Inc., Reading, Mass., 1949. A standard treatment of the physics of light at the second-year college level.
2. *Sci. Am.*, vol. 219, no. 3, September, 1968. An entire issue on the subject of light.
3. Seliger, H. H., and W. D. McElroy: "Light: Physical and Biological Action," Academic Press, Inc., New York, 1965. A general treatment of physical photobiology.

4. Edisbury, J. R.: "Practical Hints on Absorption Spectrometry," Hilger and Watts, Ltd., London, 1966. A most entertaining and useful book on details in the practice of absorption measurements.
5. Udenfriend, S.: "Fluorimetric Assay in Biology and Medicine," Academic Press, Inc., New York, 1962. A comprehensive volume on the techniques and applications in biology of fluorescence analysis.

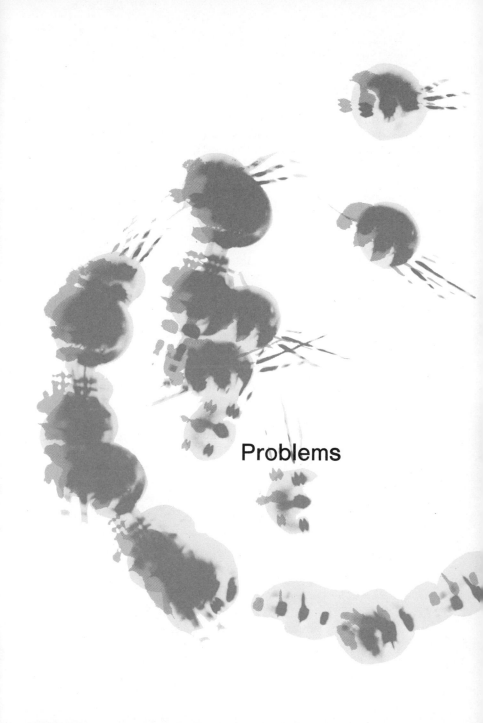

Problems

The easier problems are indicated by *; the more difficult by †. The rest are of intermediate difficulty.

* 1. A mercury lamp emits at (approximately) the following characteristic wavelengths in the visible: *405, 435,* 495, *546, 578,* 610, 623, and *691* nm. Supposing that the lamp radiates 10 watts at each of the italicized wavelengths and 2 watts at each of the others, how many einsteins/sec does it radiate in the visible?

* 2. A parallel beam of light has an intensity of 1 watt/cm². A small plane surface in the beam is oriented so that its perpendicular makes an angle θ with the direction of the beam. What is the radiant flux through this surface in watts/cm²?

† 3. A thin tubular lamp 2 feet long radiates 1 candle per inch of its length. Compute the luminous intensity in foot candles at a point 1 foot from the center of the lamp, equidistant from the ends. (Imagine, at the specified point, a small element of surface perpendicular to a line from the center of the lamp. Compute the flux through this element.) Repeat the calculation for an infinitely long lamp.

* 4. Compute A and T for OD = 0, 0.1, 0.3, 1, 2, and 3. Sketch A and T versus OD.

* 5. Show that Eq. (3-3) leads directly to Eq. (3-13).

* 6. Show that if concentration is expressed in milligrams/liter and path length is in centimeters, the extinction coefficient ϵ has units of cm²/μg if the liter is equated to 1,000 cm³.

7. Chlorophylls *a* and *b*, two types of chlorophyll, have the following extinction coefficients for the pigments dissolved in acetone.

	ϵ, $cm^2/\mu g$, at	
Type	*645 nm*	*662 nm*
Chl *a*	0.017	0.082
Chl *b*	0.045	0.010

A particular sample, held in a cell of 1-cm path length, has an
OD of 0.50 at 645 nm and 1.00 at 662 nm. What are the concentrations of chlorophylls *a* and *b* in the sample?

8. Two substances A and B are dissolved together at concentrations
[A] and [B]. The path length is 1 cm. The extinction coefficients
are $\epsilon_1{}^A$ and $\epsilon_1{}^B$ at wavelength λ_1, and $\epsilon_2{}^A$ and $\epsilon_2{}^B$ at λ_2. The
OD's measured at λ_1 and λ_2 are OD_1 and OD_2. Derive a formula
for [A] and one for [B], each in terms of the ϵ's and OD's. The
correct formulas should give the right answers in Prob. 7 above.

9. Imagine that molecules are tiny black (perfectly absorbing)
spheres of cross section *S*. Then in the very dilute limit, such
that no sphere shades another in a light beam, the fraction of
light absorbed equals the fraction of the area that is occupied
by the spheres:

$$\frac{-dI}{I} = (\text{number of spheres per unit area}) \times (\text{area } S \text{ of one sphere})$$

The quantity *S* is the "absorption cross section" of the molecule.
Show that

$$S \text{ (cm}^2 \text{ per molecule)} = 0.38 \times 10^{-20} \, \epsilon \, (M^{-1} \, cm^{-1})$$

For chlorophyll *a* at the wavelength of maximum absorption (about 660 nm in ether), $\epsilon = 10^5$ M^{-1} cm^{-1}. Compute S and compare it with the actual size of the molecule, which is about 20×20 Å except for a long hydrocarbon "tail."

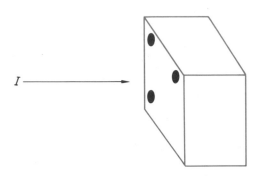

10. On the average, how often does a single molecule of chlorophyll *a* absorb a quantum of red light (660 nm) in a beam of intensity 10^{-3} watt/cm²? Use the data of Prob. 9.

*11. A uniform layer of light-absorbing material has an OD of 0.30. Now the light-absorbing stuff is crowded into half of the former cross section:

Before:

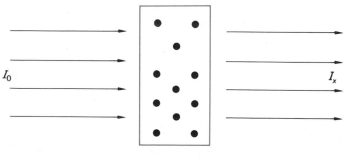

(OD = 0.30)

After:

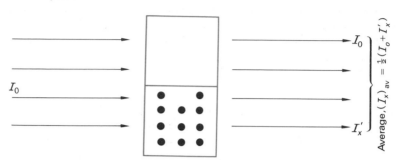

a. Compute OD_{av}, defined operationally as log $[I_0/(I_x)_{av}]$.

b. If this crowding is continued until the material occupies a very small space, what limit does the measured OD_{av} approach?

†12. Assume that an integrating sphere (Fig. 3-10) works "perfectly" in the sense that the radiation is distributed uniformly in the sphere. The detector then samples a certain fraction of the total quanta Q in the sphere: detector signal is proportional to Q. Quanta enter the sphere (incoming beam) at a rate I_0. They are disposed of, or quenched, by two processes:

a. Absorption on the first pass through the sample, at a rate AI_0. This happens only if the incoming beam hits the sample. The fraction absorbed A is the quantity that we wish to measure.

b. Absorption by the walls and by the sample *after* the first pass and subsequent reflections, and exit through the ports. This happens whether the incoming beam hits the sample or not. This combination of loss processes has a rate proportional to Q.

Two measurements are made, one (hit) in which the incoming beam hits the sample and a second (miss) in which it does not. In a steady state a certain level of radiation, Q(hit) or Q(miss), is established, as determined by the condition that quanta are being quenched or lost at the same rate that they are entering. Show that

$$\frac{\text{Detector signal (hit)}}{\text{Detector signal (miss)}} = 1 - A$$

13. The accompanying sketch shows an absorption band of a pigment, plotted as ϵ versus the wave number k. This band represents a transition from the ground state to the lowest excited state. The corresponding downward transition is accompanied by the emission of fluorescence. In a measurement of fluorescence yield it was found that for every 50 quanta absorbed by the pigment, one quantum was emitted as fluorescence. Compute the mean actual lifetime of the pigment in its lowest excited state.

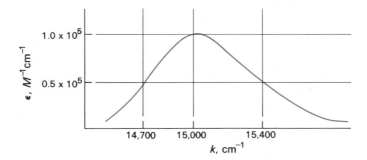

14. Consider a photochemical system with rate constants k_f, k_d, and k_p for the processes by which excited molecules follow the paths of fluorescence, radiationless deexcitation, and photochemistry

respectively. The quantum efficiencies for fluorescence and photochemistry, ϕ_f and ϕ_p, are given by Eq. (3-18). Suppose a photochemical poison is added to the system, with the result that k_p becomes zero and ϕ_f takes on a new value $\phi_f{}^0$. Show that

$$\phi_p = 1 - \frac{\phi_f}{\phi_f{}^0}$$

This problem illustrates how a system can be manipulated so that measurements of *relative* fluorescence efficiency (the ratio of ϕ_f to $\phi_f{}^0$) can give the *absolute* photochemical efficiency.

†15. Consider the photochemical system of Fig. 2-27*b*, with S and D in solution. Assume that the reaction $S^* + D \rightarrow S^- + D^+$ requires a collision between S^* (excited S) and D. Think about the way in which photochemical efficiency ought to depend on the concentration of D; on the concentration of S. Express your thoughts by crude sketches, anticipating the form of ϕ_p versus [D] at constant [S] and ϕ_p versus [S] at constant [D]. Repeat these considerations with the added complication that S and D can form a dissociable complex:

$$S + D \rightleftarrows S \cdot D$$

Assume that excitation of the complex leads unfailingly to the photochemical event: $S^* \cdot D \rightarrow S^- + D^+$. Assume that a dissociation constant exists for the complex:

$$\frac{[S][D]}{[S \cdot D]} = K$$

16. The quantum efficiency for photosynthetic oxygen evolution by a suspension of algae was to be measured by Warburg

manometry. The instrument (Fig. 3-16) was first calibrated as follows. Fifty milligrams of hydrazine sulfate, $N_2H_4\cdot H_2SO_4$, was dissolved in 100 ml of 0.1 N sulfuric acid. In the manometer vessel, 2.7 ml of this solution was mixed with 0.3 ml of 0.1 M potassium iodate solution. Nitrogen was evolved by the reaction

$$3N_2H_4\cdot H_2SO_4 + 2KIO_3 \;\rightarrow\; 2KI + 3H_2SO_4 + 6H_2O + 3N_2$$

The pressure change due to this nitrogen evolution was measured while the vessel was shaken in a bath at 30°C. The change amounted to 98 mm of manometer fluid (the fluid is water with a little detergent and a dye for visibility). A second vessel, to be used as a control, gave the same pressure change in a similar calibration.

Now 2.7 ml of a dense suspension of the algae was placed in the first vessel, and 2.7 ml of water in the second. The center well of each contained 0.3 ml of a bicarbonate buffer. The purpose of the control vessel with water (called a thermobarometer) is to register nonessential changes due to small fluctuations in temperature and atmospheric pressure. In processing the data, these changes should be subtracted from the changes shown by the reaction vessel.

The vessels were shaken in the 30° bath, and after a period of recording oxygen uptake due to respiration in the dark, a light was turned onto the vessels and the measurement was continued. After the photosynthetic oxygen evolution had been recorded for a time, the light was turned off again. The light was of wavelength 434 nm, isolated from the spectrum of a mercury arc by means of color filters. It struck the vessels from below; its intensity as measured at the bottom of the reaction vessel was 2.0×10^{-4} watt/cm^2. The area of the bottom of the vessel was 8.2 cm^2, not counting the center well from which the algae were excluded. Four percent of the light impinging on the vessel was lost by reflections at the glass surfaces; the rest (within the 8.2 cm^2 occupied by the algae) was absorbed.

The following data were obtained:

Time, min	Operation	Pressure in reaction vessel, mm manometer fluid above atmospheric	Pressure in control vessel containing water
0		0	0
5		−1	0
10		0	1
15		−2	0
20		−2	1
25		−4	0
30		−5	−1
35		−5	−1
40		−7	−2
45	Light on	−8	−2
50		−6	−2
55		−3	−2
60		−2	−2
65		1	−1
70		4	0
75		5	0
80		7	1
85		8	0
90		9	0
95	Light off	12	1
100		12	1
105		9	0
110		8	0
115		9	1
120		7	0
125		7	0
130		6	0

Plot the data, evaluate the rates of oxygen consumption or evolution, and compute the quantum efficiency for photosynthetic oxygen evolution, expressed as molecules of oxygen per quantum. Assume that the respiratory oxygen uptake, as measured in the dark, continued at the same rate during the light period. The rate of oxygen evolution due to photosynthesis is then the algebraic difference between the rates measured in the light and in dark.

17. In an experiment, as illustrated in Figs. 3-17 and 3-18, the "light on" and "light off" slopes were measured to be $\Delta OD/sec = -0.0013$ and -0.0011 respectively. The differential extinction coefficient for cytochrome oxidation at 550 nm, from Fig. 3-10, is -17×10^3 M^{-1} cm^{-1}. The sample was adjusted so as to absorb 30 percent of the 880-nm exciting light. The incident exciting light intensity was 3.7×10^{-5} watt/cm^2 *after* reflection losses had been discounted. Compute the quantum efficiency for cytochrome oxidation in the dark-adapted preparation and in the illuminated steady state.

18. Refer to the experimental construction of Fig. 3-17. Let the sample cuvette have dimensions x, y, and z in centimeters: x along the axis of the measuring beam, y along the axis of the exciting beam, and z in height (assume that the height z is encompassed by both the measuring beam and the exciting beam). Show that Eq. (3-22) must be modified by the factor y/x:

$$\phi_p = \frac{y}{x} \frac{\Delta OD/sec}{10^3 I_0 A \, \Delta \epsilon}$$

*19. Refer to Fig. 3-19, and imagine that the peak absorption at λ_1 is 20 percent, that at λ_2 is 16 percent, and the minimum between these peaks is 5 percent. Now suppose that the action spectrum measurement is repeated with a sample 25 times as concentrated. Sketch the expected absorption and action spectra.

Answers
to Problems

1. 2.5×10^{-4} einsteins/sec
2. $\cos \theta$
3. 17 foot candles, 24 foot candles
7. 11.4 μg/ml chlorophyll *a*, 6.8 μg/ml chlorophyll *b*
9. $S = 3.8$ Å^2
10. Once every 0.8 sec
11. *a.* 0.20
    b. zero
13. 4×10^{-10} sec
15. *Partial answer*: Without complex formation, ϕ_p is more or less independent of the concentration of S. With complex formation, ϕ_p decreases at sufficiently high concentrations of the sensitizing pigment. Furthermore the efficiency can be high even if collisions of D with S* are rare, if complexing occurs.
16. 13.5 percent
17. 0.95, 0.80
19. *Partial answer*: Peak absorptions 99.6 and 98.7 percent; minimum between peaks 72 percent.

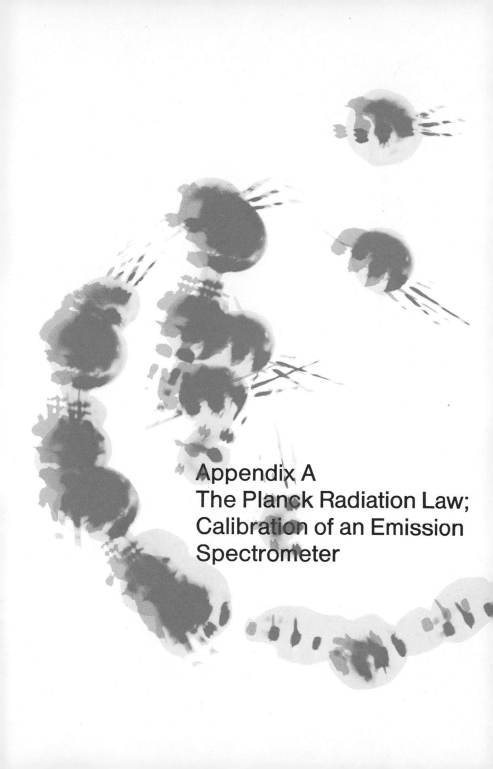

Appendix A
The Planck Radiation Law;
Calibration of an Emission
Spectrometer

THE PLANCK RADIATION LAW; CALIBRATION
OF AN EMISSION SPECTROMETER

To the physicist an ideal blackbody is a perfect absorber and emitter, fairly well aproximated by a carbon lamp filament. It has no special color: no special tendency to absorb or emit light in any particular region of wavelength or frequency. A blackbody can be regarded as having a continuous distribution of possible energy states. Transitions among these states involve the absorption and emission of quanta, covering the whole spectrum of frequencies from zero to infinity. As the temperature of the body is raised, higher energy states come into play in greater numbers and so the transitions involve quanta of progressively higher frequencies (shorter wavelengths). This causes the changes in color of an incandescent body as it is heated: from black (infrared) through red, orange, and yellow, to blue-white at several thousand degrees.

The spectrum of radiation associated with a blackbody is described as follows. Imagine a cavity inside a blackbody at absolute temperature T. Radiation is continually being emitted and absorbed at the surface of the cavity, so that an equilibrium is established between radiation inside the cavity and energy states in the material of the blackbody. Under this equilibrium condition the radiation is distributed among frequencies according to Planck's law:

$$E_\nu = \frac{8\pi h}{c^3} \frac{\nu^3}{e^{h\nu/kT} - 1} \tag{A-1}$$

E_ν is the density of radiant energy within the cavity, ergs/cm^3 per unit interval of frequency. The constants are:

$h = $ Planck's constant, 6.6×10^{-27} erg sec

$c = $ the speed of light in vacuum, 3×10^{10} cm/sec

$k = $ Boltzmann's constant, 1.38×10^{-16} erg/degree

and the temperature T is in degrees Kelvin ($^\circ$K $= ^\circ$C $+ 273$).

The density of energy between the frequencies ν and $\nu + d\nu$ is then given by

$$dE = E_\nu \, d\nu$$

and the density between frequencies ν_1 and ν_2 is

$$E = \int_{\nu_1}^{\nu_2} E_\nu \, d\nu$$

The total energy density of all frequencies is

$$E_{\text{tot}} = \int_0^\infty E_\nu \, d\nu = 7.6 \times 10^{-15} T^4 \text{ erg/cm}^3 \qquad \text{(A-2)}$$

Equation (A-1) can be put in terms of quanta/cm^3, rather than ergs/cm^3, by dividing it by the energy of one quantum, $h\nu$:

$$Q_\nu(\text{quanta/cm}^3) = \frac{E_\nu(\text{ergs/cm}^3)}{h\nu} = \frac{8\pi}{c^3} \frac{\nu^2}{e^{h\nu/kT} - 1} \qquad \text{(A-3)}$$

To translate these formulas from frequency to wavelength, we use $\nu = c/\lambda$ and correspondingly $d\nu = -c \, d\lambda/\lambda^2$. The minus sign simply means that frequency decreases as wavelength increases, and can be dropped. Equation (A-1) then becomes

$$E_\lambda = 8\pi hc \, \frac{\lambda^{-5}}{e^{hc/\lambda kT} - 1} \qquad \text{(A-4)}$$

for the energy density per unit interval of wavelength, and Eq. (A-3) becomes

$$Q_\lambda = \frac{8\pi \lambda^{-4}}{e^{hc/\lambda kT} - 1} \qquad \text{(A-5)}$$

for the quantum density per unit wavelength interval.

For T near room temperature (about $300°K$) and frequencies in the optical range, $e^{h\nu/kT} \gg 1$ and the following simplifications can be made:

$$\text{Eq. (A-1) becomes} \quad E_\nu = \frac{8\pi h}{c^3} \nu^3 \exp\frac{-h\nu}{kT} \qquad (A-6)$$

$$\text{(A-3) becomes} \quad Q_\nu = \frac{8\pi}{c^3} \nu^2 \exp\frac{-h\nu}{kT} \qquad (A-7)$$

$$\text{(A-4) becomes} \quad E_\lambda = 8\pi hc\lambda^{-5} \exp\frac{-hc}{\lambda kT} \qquad (A-8)$$

$$\text{(A-5) becomes} \quad Q_\lambda = 8\pi\lambda^{-4} \exp\frac{-hc}{\lambda kT} \qquad (A-9)$$

By differentiating Eqs. (A-8) and (A-9) with respect to λ and setting the derivative equal to zero, one can show that the functions E_λ and Q_λ are maximal at wavelengths (in nanometers) equal to $2.9 \times 10^6/T$ and $3.6 \times 10^6/T$ respectively (Wien's law). For a tungsten lamp operated at $2900°K$ this puts the maximum in the near infrared, at 1,000 nm for the energy curve and 1,240 nm for the quantum curve.

The radiant flux leaving the surface of a blackbody is proportional to the density of radiation within the cavity, so in any experimental construction involving a blackbody as a lamp, the emission spectrum is given [from Eq. (A-9)] by

$$I_\lambda = A\lambda^{-4} \exp\frac{-hc}{\lambda kT} \qquad (A-10)$$

where I_λ is the intensity in units proportional to quanta/cm² sec, T is the temperature of the lamp filament and A is a numerical constant. With λ expressed in nanometers and T in $°K$ the argument of the exponential factor, $-hc/\lambda kT$, reduces to $-1.44 \times 10^7/\lambda T$.

An actual lamp filament is not an ideal blackbody. Its emission spectrum deviates from that given by Eq. (A-10), but at some temperature (T') its color will be indistinguishable to the eye from that of a blackbody at temperature T. It is then said to have a "color temperature" T. A small tungsten projection lamp in the neighborhood of 30 watts, such as the General Electric Type BVB, has a color temperature of about 2800°K when operated near its rated voltage (2860°K for the General Electric BVB driven at 120 volts).

Now suppose that we have built an emission spectrometer such that light coming from a sample is analyzed by passing it through a monochromator and on to a light detector (see Fig. 3-13). The spectrum of emission recorded in this way will be distorted by two factors: Both the efficiency of the monochromator and the sensitivity of the detector will vary with wavelength. This distortion can be measured and then taken into account by recording the response of the system to a known emission spectrum. A very convenient known spectrum is that from a tungsten lamp of specified color temperature. One simply puts this lamp in place of the sample. The spectrum is computed from Eq. (A-10) and can be normalized (by suitable choice of the numerical constant A) to agree with the recorded spectrum at some particular wavelength. The correction factor at any other wavelength is then simply the ratio of the computed to the recorded value.

Appendix B
A Relationship
between
Absorption and
Fluorescence

A RELATIONSHIP BETWEEN ABSORPTION
AND FLUORESCENCE

For some molecules the shape and position of a fluorescence band can be computed from that of the corresponding absorption band through a simple thermodynamic argument. This argument has been published several times during this century, and yet most chemists and physicists seem unaware of its existence. For a more extended discussion of its history see R. T. Ross and M. Calvin, *Biophysical Journal*, vol. 7, p. 595, 1967.

Consider a molecule with a ground state and a lowest excited state, as sketched in Fig. 2-17, and imagine a collection of such molecules inside a cavity in a blackbody at temperature T (see Appendix A), in thermal equilibrium with the blackbody. Detailed thermal equilibrium implies that for each upward transition in the set of molecules there is a downward transition spanning the same energy gap.[1] Therefore the distribution of downward transitions (the fluorescence spectrum) can be computed from that of the upward transitions. The relative probabilities of upward transitions of different wavelengths are given by the product of the absorption (or extinction) coefficient of the molecule and the radiation density at each wavelength. Equating the probability of absorption (upward transitions) to that of fluorescence (downward transitions) and using Eq. (A-9) (Appendix A) for the radiation density we have

$$f_\lambda = \epsilon_\lambda Q_\lambda = 8\pi\epsilon_\lambda\lambda^{-4}\exp\frac{-hc}{\lambda kT} \qquad \text{(B-1)}$$

for the relative fluorescence at wavelength λ, in units proportional to quanta per unit wavelength interval. In this formula ϵ_λ is the extinction coefficient (see Sec. 3-3) of the molecule at wavelength λ. This relationship has more commonly been expressed in terms of frequency, using Eq. (A-7) instead of (A-9):

$$f_\nu = C\nu^2\epsilon_\nu\exp\frac{-h\nu}{kT} \qquad \text{(B-2)}$$

---

[1] If this were not so, the entropy of the system would be changing.

where C is an arbitrary numerical constant since we are only dealing with *relative* fluorescence intensities. In Eq. (B-2) the fluorescence is in units proportional to quanta per unit interval of frequency. This equation can be rearranged to the logarithmic form

$$\log_{10} \frac{\nu^2 \epsilon_\nu}{f_\nu} = \frac{h}{2.3kT} \nu + C' \qquad \text{(B-3)}$$

where $C' = -\log_{10} C$.

So far we have derived the spectrum of fluorescence of a collection of molecules in thermal equilibrium inside a blackbody at temperature T. If T represents room temperature, the inside of the blackbody is nearly dark: There is very little radiation in the visible part of the spectrum. Then if the absorption and fluorescence bands of the molecule are in or near the visible region, the major transitions (between electronic ground and excited states) are rare and the fraction of molecules in the excited state is extremely small.

The speed with which thermal equilibrium is attained depends on the rate at which energy is exchanged between the blackbody, the radiation field, and the molecules in the cavity. At room temperature this process is relatively fast for the small transitions between the sublevels of major electronic states, because radiation quanta of the appropriate energy are relatively abundant and much slower for the larger transitions between electronic ground and excited states. Therefore if the system is changed suddenly, say, by an abrupt change in the temperature of the blackbody, the distribution of energies among sublevels of either the ground or the excited state will come to a correspondence with thermal equilibrium much sooner than the coarser partition between these major states. One way to disturb the system is to cut a hole in the blackbody and shine a light into the cavity. This will suddenly increase the population of excited-state molecules by a large factor. If the light is cut off, the excess population in the excited state will eventually subside to the ground state. But from the foregoing argument, this new excited-state population will reach thermal equilibrium among its own sublevels long before it has begun to decay appreciably. This equilibrium distribution has, therefore, the same form as that reached in the "dark" case where the excited-state population is much smaller. It is the form of this distribution that dictates the shape of the fluorescence spectrum, and so the spectrum computed by Eq. (B-1) or (B-2) will be correct regardless of how the molecules have been put into the excited state.

This argument has shown how the fluorescence spectrum can be computed *if* the excited-state population can attain thermal equilibrium among its own sublevels during its lifetime. This will generally be true for strongly fluorescent pigments, whose excited-state lifetime is about 10^{-8} sec or more. A test is to measure both the absorption spectrum and the fluorescence spectrum and then to plot $\log_{10} (\nu^2 \epsilon_\nu / f_\nu)$ against ν, as suggested by Eq. (B-3). This semilogarithmic plot should yield a straight line of slope $h/2.3kT$, where T is the temperature of the room.

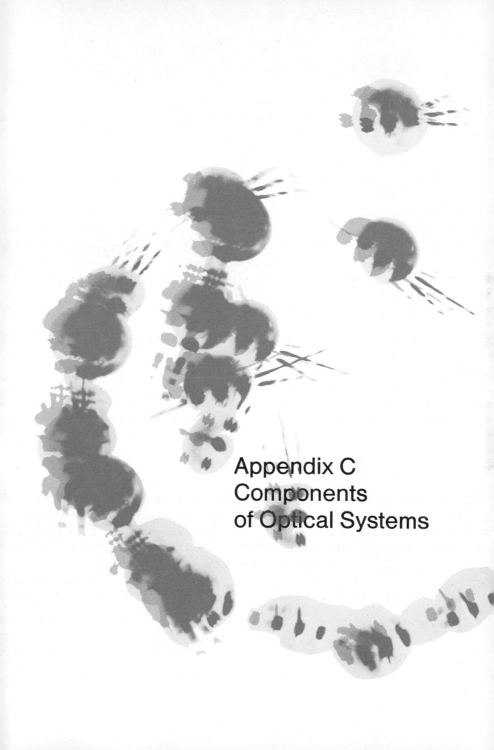

Appendix C
Components
of Optical Systems

COMPONENTS OF OPTICAL SYSTEMS

The components needed for research in photochemistry and photobiology fall into the following broad categories:

1. Lenses, mirrors, prisms, shutters and other small components
2. Optical filters and monochromators
3. Lamps
4. Light detectors
5. Electronic accessories: voltage supplies and regulators, amplifiers, and recorders

A framework for discussing these components is provided by the homemade apparatus shown in Figs. C-1 and C-2. This apparatus illustrates many of the operating principles of the more expensive and elaborate commercial absorption and fluorescence spectrometers; see the legend of Fig. C-1. The basic elements shown here can also be arranged in other configurations as the need arises in connection with particular experiments.

The ensuing description of components will include many references to commercial sources and brands. These references will indicate just a few out of many possible and often equally suitable sources. They are mentioned for the convenience of the reader, but often there is nothing special about the particular choice except that it falls within the author's personal experience.

Simple lenses, front-surface mirrors, prisms, and other small optical components can be obtained most cheaply from companies such as Edmund Scientific Co., Barrington, N.J., that began by salvaging surplus military equipment. Photographic equipment including shutters and certain lamps can be ordered through local camera shops or from a major distributor such as Burke and James, Inc., Chicago. The mounting of these components can be improvised, or else certain sources of costlier mounted optical equipment can be used (for example, J. Klinger, Jamaica, N.Y., distributors for Spindler and Höyer). A useful source of optical mounting benches and components, including flat-sided glass cells to hold water as a heat filter,

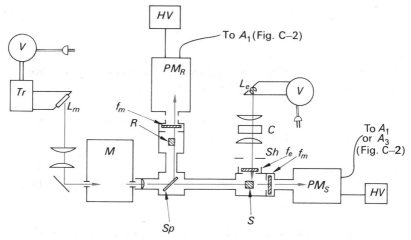

Fig. C-1.   Schematic diagram of a simple instrument for measuring optical absorption (optical density OD), light-induced changes in OD, and fluorescence.

V = variable transformer
Tr = 6-volt, 20-ampere transformer
L_m = measuring lamp (ribbon filament, 6 volt, 18 ampere)
M = monochromator
Sp = beam splitter (semitransparent mirror)
R = reference path cell
f_m = measuring beam filter
PM_R = reference beam detector (photomultiplier)
HV = high-voltage supply for photomultiplier
S = sample cell
PM_S = sample beam detector (photomultiplier)
L_e = excitation lamp (quartz-iodine, 650 watt)
C = glass cell for water to cool excitation beam
Sh = excitation beam shutter
f_e = excitation beam filter
A_1 — operational amplifier, logarithmic conversion (see Fig. C-2)
A_3 = operational amplifier, electrometer (see Fig. C-2)
Lenses shown in profile

For absorption measurements a monochromatic beam of measuring light is split into two by a semitransparent mirror. One of the two beams is sent through a sample cell and to a detector (photomultiplier) and the other through a reference cell and to a detector. The photocurrents generated by the two beams are fed to an amplifier A_1 that registers the logarithm of their ratio and hence the OD of the sample. The output of A_1 is amplified further and then recorded; see Fig. C-2. Changes in OD of the sample induced by the excitation beam can also be recorded. By turning off the measuring beam, any fluorescence of the sample evoked by the excitation beam can be detected, with the output of the detector (PM_S) fed into another amplifier (see Fig. C-2). In some of these applications it is necessary to protect the detectors from scattered exciting light by means of complementary filters f_e and f_m. To measure the spectrum of fluorescence, one must move the monochromator to a position between the sample cell and PM_S.

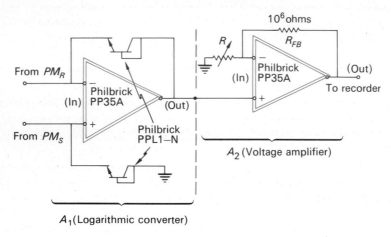

Absorption measurement

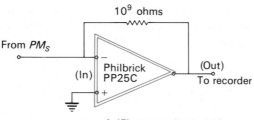

Fluorescence measurement

Fig. C-2. Amplifying systems for use with the instrument shown in Fig. C-1 (some familiarity with basic electronics is assumed here). The triangles denote operational amplifiers. These are high-gain amplifiers that employ nearly 100 percent negative feedback. The result is that the input-output relationship is determined almost entirely by the circuit element(s) in the feedback branch. A major vendor of such amplifiers is Philbrick Researches, Inc., Dedham, Mass. In circuit A_1 the output in volts equals $0.06 \log_{10}(i_R/i_S)$, where i_R and i_S are the reference and sample photocurrents respectively. A_2 is a voltage amplifier whose gain equals $1 + R_{FB}/R$. A_3 is a so-called electrometer amplifier; volts (out) $= R_{FB} \times$ current (in). A suitable recorder for many applications is the Bausch and Lomb Type VOM-5.

is Central Scientific, Chicago. This company also sells a beeswax-like substance called Tackiwax, indispensible for securing components onto a table quickly but reversibly. Other materials of considerable utility in experimental optics are epoxy cement, black plastic electrical tape, black cloth (both cotton and felt), flat black spray-on paint, black cardboard (from an art supply store), and toilet paper rolls.

It is well to enclose the light-sensitive parts of the system in a train of boxes and tubes, as indicated in Fig. C-1, so that the work need not be conducted in a darkroom. Successive components can be joined by taping around the ends of tubes. These light shields can be machined nicely from metal or cut crudely out of black cardboard, depending on taste and on the desire for permanence.

The spectral composition of light is controlled by means of monochromators and optical filters. A monochromator uses a prism or a diffraction grating to spread a thin strip of light into a spectrum of its component colors. Any desired part of this spectrum is then selected by means of a slit. The grating monochromator offers the convenience that the dispersion of the spectrum is uniform, so that position along the spectrum is proportional to wavelength. The prism instrument transmits a smaller proportion of stray light, of unwanted wavelengths. Small grating monochromators suitable for most applications in photobiology are made by Bausch and Lomb, Rochester, N.Y., and by Jarrell-Ash Co., Waltham, Mass. A good prism monochromator is offered by the Leiss Company, distributed by the Photovolt Corp., New York.

Optical filters are principally of two types: those relying on absorption by pigments and those based on constructive and destructive interference of multiply reflected light waves. The *interference filters* can be designed to transmit very narrow intervals of wavelength, so a complete set of these is equivalent to a monochromator. In Fig. C-1 the measuring beam filters f_m might well be interference filters whose wavelength for transmission matches the measuring wavelength passed by the monochromator, and the excitation filter f_e an interference filter of another wavelength, suitable for excitation.

The quality of an interference filter depends strongly on the degree to which transmission of unwanted wavelengths has been suppressed, and this cannot always be learned from the manufacturer's specifications. A reliable source of interference filters at this writing is Baird-Atomic, Inc., Cambridge, Mass.

Colored glass absorption filters are sold by Corning Glass Works, Corning, N.Y., and by Schott, distributed by Fish-Schurman Corp., New Rochelle, N.Y. A colored gelatin sheet that can be mounted between glass is the basis of the Wratten filters sold by Eastman Kodak, Rochester, N.Y. A general property of absorption filters is that they transmit a broad region of the spectrum and do not exhibit a sharp cutoff on the long-wavelength side of the transmission band. They can be made to cut off sharply on the short-wave side of the band.

In addition to color filters there are neutral (gray) filters that are used to attenuate a beam of light more or less uniformly at all wavelengths. These can be made of uniformly exposed photographic plates, of blackened screens, and of semitransparent mirrors. The semitransparent mirrors, which are also useful as beam splitters, are made by depositing a thin film of aluminum on a glass surface.

The measuring beam in the apparatus of Fig. C-1 is generated by a tungsten lamp with a ribbon filament; the image of the filament fits the entrance slit of the monochromator. A suitable lamp is the General Electric Type 18A/T10/1P Microscope Illuminator, which draws 18 amps at 6 volts. Central Scientific of Chicago sells a convenient holder for lamps of this type. The large filament of a low-voltage, high-current lamp has two advantages: It is less susceptible to vibrations, and its high heat capacity helps to prevent short-term fluctuations of intensity caused by variations of the voltage. Also, because the outline of the uniformly bright filament can be made to overlap the entrance slit of the monochromator, the system is not too sensitive to fluctuations caused by vibrations of its components.

These advantages of high stability are usually unimportant for the excitation beam, and the more intense quartz-iodine lamp is to be preferred. This is a tungsten lamp with some iodine inside a quartz envelope. The iodine reacts with tungsten to form tungsten iodide, which dissociates into the elements at higher temperatures. As a result the iodine picks up tungsten from cooler parts of the lamp and, by dissociation of the tungsten iodide, deposits the metal again on the hot filament. This "scrubbing" action allows the lamp to be burned at a higher temperature and prevents blackening of the envelope. These lamps, as well as the ribbon filament types, can be obtained at camera shops. A suitable quartz-iodine lamp, which comes with a convenient holder, is the Sylvania "Sun Gun," Type DWY (650 watts).

The foregoing lamps are useful for excitation and measurement in the visible and near infrared regions. In the ultraviolet, below about 350 nm, the emission from a tungsten lamp is too weak for most practical purposes. In that region the best choice for the measuring beam is a deuterium arc lamp, and for ultraviolet excitation the less stable but much brighter high-pressure xenon arc is useful. These ultraviolet lamps are hazardous and should be used with due respect for the danger to the eyes. They can be obtained from many sources; perhaps the greatest variety is offered by George W. Gates and Co., Franklin Square, Long Island, N.Y.

Special applications requiring flashes of very short duration lead to the use of xenon flash lamps or lasers; these will not be discussed further here.

Much can be and has been said about the merits and disadvantages of various types of light detectors. In the end, photomultipliers satisfy almost all requirements in photochemistry and photobiology. A photomultiplier has a light-sensitive metallic surface, the cathode, from which electrons are ejected by incident light quanta in the proper range of wavelength. The quantum efficiency and hence the sensitivity of the device varies with wavelength, and cathodes of different composition show different wavelength dependencies. Thus a photomultiplier should be selected to be responsive in the wavelength region of interest. Electrons ejected from the cathode of a photomultiplier are accelerated by an electric field toward another electrode called the first dynode. An electron striking this electrode causes ejection of two or more secondary electrons, which are accelerated toward another electrode (the second dynode). This electron-multiplying process is repeated through a succession of about ten dynodes, so that a single quantum of light striking the cathode causes a cascade of electrons culminating in the release of perhaps 10^5

electrons from the last dynode. A final electrode, the anode, collects these electrons; and this light-induced electric current can be measured as indicated in Fig. C-2. Details of the electrical connections to the cathode, dynodes, and anode of a photomultiplier are described in Appendix D. Two major sources of photomultipliers are RCA, Lancaster, Pa., and EMI Electronics, Ltd., distributed by Whittaker Corp. (Gencom Division), Plainview, Long Island, N.Y.

Photomultipliers are extremely sensitive and respond quickly, generally in times much smaller than a microsecond. They have one important limitation: The sensitivity varies strongly with wavelength, with operating conditions and with the past history of operation. Therefore they are poor devices for the measurement of absolute light intensity. Traditionally the detector of choice for absolute measurements has been the thermocouple (or the thermopile, several thermocouples in series). This is a junction of two dissimilar metals; such a junction has the property of maintaining an electric potential that varies with temperature. Thus a thermocouple is an electric thermometer. The junction is blackened so as to absorb radiation of all wavelengths, and the rise in temperature shows how much radiation has been absorbed. More recently thermocouples have given way to thermistors: devices whose electrical resistance varies strongly with temperature. Thermocouples and thermistors have a sensitivity that is stable and reproducible, and is independent of wavelength. Unfortunately they respond so slowly (this is a function of their heat capacity) that at very low intensities the light effect is lost in casual variations of the temperature of the surroundings. As a result, the practical limit of sensitivity without special precautions is about 10^{-5} watt/cm^2. A useful thermistor radiometer, calibrated in absolute units (watts/cm^2), is made by the Yellow Springs Instrument Co., Yellow Springs, Ohio. This device serves, for example, to measure the levels of exciting light in determinations of quantum efficiency.

Some basic electronic circuits for measuring photocurrents are shown in Fig. C-2. The operational amplifiers shown in these circuits can be obtained from Philbrick Researches, Inc., Dedham, Mass., at prices in the neighborhood of $100. The circuit of A_3 performs the basic electrometer function of converting a small current through a high resistance into a moderate voltage associated with a low resistance. A typically weak photocurrent of the order of 10^{-9} amp passing through a resistance of 10^9 ohms generates a signal of about 1 volt on the "low resistance" side of the circuit, where it is easily registered on a recorder.

The choice of a recorder depends mainly on the quickness of response that must be preserved. A great many ink-writing recorders, including the Bausch and Lomb Type VOM-5, require about 0.1 sec or more to register a change in the signal. For faster response the best choice is an oscilloscope, and with a variable-persistence screen the trace can be recorded quickly and then viewed at leisure.

Photomultipliers require variable DC power supplies that can deliver several milliamperes at voltages up to about $-1,500$ volts (the positive side is at ground potential). These can be bought from many sources for about \$300. Alternatively one can be made from several batteries (90-volt and smaller) plus some good multipole switches. In assembling such battery devices, shocks are inevitable. They are irritating but harmless *if* the operator keeps one hand behind his back so that the current is confined to the hand in use, and does not pass near the heart, brain, etc.

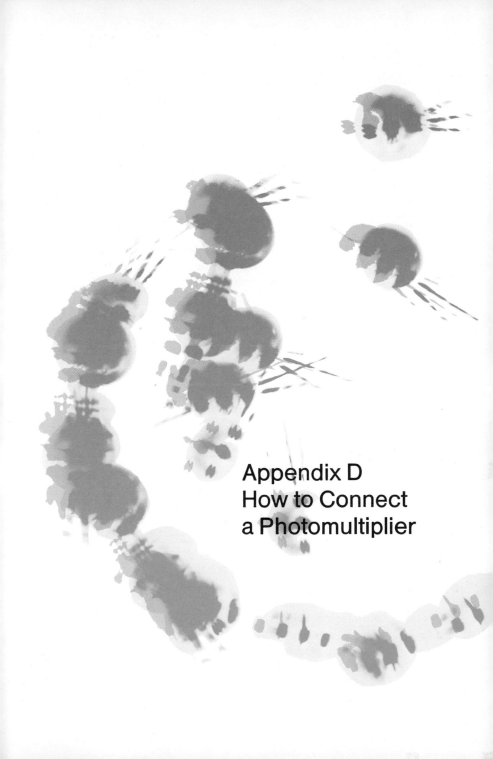

Appendix D
How to Connect
a Photomultiplier

HOW TO CONNECT A PHOTOMULTIPLIER

The proper electrical connections for a photomultiplier will be described here; the reader should first see Appendix C for a description of this device. The first dynode must be at a potential more positive than the cathode in order to attract electrons emitted by the cathode. Each succeeding dynode, and finally the anode, must be more positive than its predecessor. This is achieved with a single source of high voltage plus a network of resistors, as indicated in Fig. D-1. Negative high voltage is applied to the cathode; the positive side of the high voltage supply is at ground potential. Most photomultipliers function well if the difference in potential between cathode and first dynode is twice that between succeeding electrodes, hence the choice of $2R$ in the top part of the network. A suitable value for R is 10^5 ohms. The output of the photomultiplier depends strongly on the voltage applied to this network. In practice, values from 200 to 1,200 volts (between cathode and ground) are generally found useful.

The current of electrons i collected by the anode flows to ground through a *load resistance* R_L (Fig. D-1) and thus develops a voltage $e = iR_L$. The load resistance is often built into an *electrometer amplifier* used with the photomultiplier; in circuit A_3 of Fig. C-2 the feedback resistance R_{FB} serves this function.

In more sensitive applications the photomultiplier should be protected from the effects of external magnetic fields. This is done by surrounding the glass envelope of the photomultiplier (except the window where light enters) with a magnetic shield: a sheet of "mu-metal," a ferrous alloy of high magnetic permeability. This shield should *not* be grounded. The glass envelope of the photomultiplier drifts slowly to the potential of the cathode (negative high voltage), and if the adjacent shield is grounded, a troublesome arcing will result. The shield should be at cathode potential, with a high resistance (10^6 ohms) between the shield and the high voltage supply, as shown in Fig. D-1. This high resistance will protect the operator and the system by limiting the current in the event of an accidental contact with the shield. The magnetic shield should of course be well insulated from the surrounding box, which is usually at ground potential.

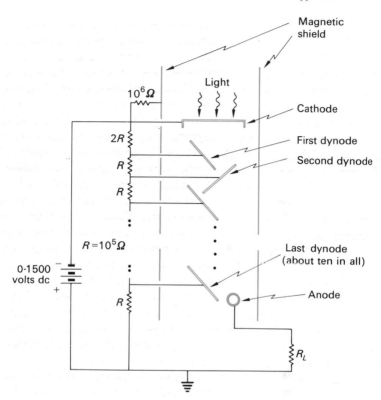

Fig. D-1. *Electrical connections to a photomultiplier. The details are discussed in the text of Appendixes C and D.*

A decided improvement in the performance of a photomultiplier can be achieved by cooling it with dry ice or with a cold stream of gas from a liquid nitrogen reservoir. This is especially necessary in measuring weak light with photomultipliers that are sensitive to the near infrared (cathodes with the so-called S-1 spectral response). The photomultiplier must then be held in an insulated box with a non-fogging (double or triple) window to admit light.

Index